Developing Lite

TEXT LEVEL

TEXT-LEVEL ACTIVITIES FOR THE LITERACY HOUR

year

Ray Barker
Christine Moorcroft

A & C BLACK

Reprinted 2000, 2001
Published 2000 by
A&C Black (Publishers) Limited
37 Soho Square, London W1D 3QZ

ISBN 0-7136-5320-5

Acknowledgements

The authors and publishers are grateful for permission to reproduce the following:

page 13: extract from 'The Fly' by Walter de la Mare by permission of The Literary Trustees of Walter de la Mare, and the Society of Authors as their representative;
page 29: extract from 'The Listeners' by Walter de la Mare by permission of The Literary Trustees of Walter de la Mare, and the Society of Authors as their representative;
page 30: extract from *The Otterbury Incident* by C Day-Lewis by permission of The Peters Fraser & Dunlop Group Ltd;
page 32: 'Fireworks' by James Reeves © James Reeves from *Complete Poems for Children* (Heinemann). Reprinted by permission of the James Reeves Estate;
page 41: extract from 'A Rainy Day' by David Orme published 1994 by Collins Educational in the Pathways series;
page 45: diagram adapted from a leaflet published by The London Wildlife Trust;
page 62: 'Workhouse Menu' from *History of Enfield Volume II* by David Pam, published by the Enfield Preservation Society.

Every effort has been made to trace copyright holders and to obtain their permission for use of copyright material. The authors and publishers would be pleased to rectify in future editions any error or omission.

The authors and publishers would like to thank the following teachers for their advice in producing this series of books:

Jane Beynon; Hardip Channa; Ann Hart; Lydia Hunt;
Rita Leader; Madeleine Madden; Helen Mason; Kim Pérez;
Joanne Turpin; Fleur Whatley

A CIP catalogue record for this book is available from the British Library.

Printed in Great Britain by
St Edmundsbury Press Ltd, Bury St Edmunds, Suffolk.

Contents

Introduction

Developing Literacy: Text Level supports the teaching of reading and writing by providing a series of activities to develop children's ability to recognise and appreciate the different genres, styles and purposes of text. **Year 5** encourages them to read texts from a variety of genres (both non-fiction and fiction), looking at characters, settings, point of view and the way narrative is built up. It develops their enjoyment of stories and poetry and provides frameworks which help them to compose their own. It also provides structures on which they can base their non-fiction writing for particular purposes.

The children learn about different kinds of text, including stories and poems by significant writers, playscripts, newspaper articles and longer classic poetry. They are also given the opportunity to encounter everyday texts used in familiar situations (for example, instructions, reports and arguments) as well as to analyse the impact of language in poetry, arguments and stories, and myths and legends from a variety of cultures.

The activities are designed to be carried out in the time allocated to independent work during the Literacy Hour. They support the objectives of the National Literacy Strategy *Framework for Teaching* at text level and they incorporate strategies which encourage independent learning, for example, ways in which children can check their own work or that of a partner.

Investigation is given greater emphasis as the series progresses towards **Year 6**.

Year 5 helps children to:

- investigate the features of good openings in stories;
- explore how characters are presented through action, dialogue and description;
- explore narrative order and plan stories;
- write playscripts and poems for performance;
- look closely at a variety of poetic forms and write their own poems;
- identify different types of non-fiction text and comment on content, structure and vocabulary;
- recognise the ways in which texts are written for particular readers;
- describe and review their own reading habits;
- make notes in a variety of ways and summarise ideas;
- edit and review their own writing.

Year 5 also develops the children's ability to:

- identify features of non-fiction texts;
- understand and use the terms *bias*, *fact* and *opinion*;
- write in a variety of forms, such as explanations, instructions and non-chronological reports;
- experiment with, and adapt, different poetic forms;
- understand how descriptive and figurative language can create moods;
- identify and use patterns of rhyme and verse and to write poetry based on particular structures;
- argue a point of view using appropriate language.

Extension

Most of the activity sheets end with a challenge **(Now try this!)** which reinforces and extends the children's learning and provides the teacher with an opportunity for assessment. These more challenging activities might be appropriate for only a few children; it is not expected that the whole class should complete them. On most pages there is space for the children to complete the activities, but for others they will need a notebook or separate sheet of paper.

Organisation

Few resources are needed besides scissors, glue, a variety of text-types (such as newspapers and leaflets), word-banks and a range of dictionaries. The activities have all been designed for use in conjunction with readily available texts of your choice.

To help teachers to select appropriate learning experiences for their pupils, the activities are grouped into sections within each book. The pages need not be presented in the order in which they appear in the books, unless otherwise stated.

Teachers' notes

Brief notes are provided at the bottom of most pages. They give ideas and suggestions for making the most of the activity sheet. They sometimes make suggestions for the whole class introduction, the plenary session or, possibly, for follow-up work using an adapted version of the activity sheet.

Structure of the Literacy Hour

The following chart shows an example of the way in which an activity from this book can be used to achieve the required organisation of the Literacy Hour.

Writing from a point of view (page 38)

Whole class introduction **15 min**

Show the class a picture of a cow and ask them to list things they notice about it. Then ask them how they feel about the animal. Do they like cows? Do they think they are smelly? Are any of the children vegetarians? How might this change their point of view? Introduce one of the characters on the sheet, for example the city-lover. What does the picture tell us about her point of view? Why should she feel this way?

Whole class activity **15 min**

Give the class another point of view, such as the scientist's. How does the scientist see the cow? Compare to the city-lover. Ask children to list words both people would use to describe the cow. How and why are they different?

Group work **20 min**

In pairs, or with the teacher in guided writing time, the children write a description of the cow from one of the points of view, carefully choosing language that person might use.

Independent work **20 min**

The others work independently from **Writing from a point of view** (page 38, **Developing Literacy: Text Level Year 5**).

Whole class plenary session **10 min**

The children read their descriptions of the same animal and others in the class guess what their point of view is. Discuss why the descriptions are different and how the words they have chosen show how they feel.

Using the activity sheets

Fiction and poetry: reading comprehension

Ways of opening stories (page 9) enables the children to discuss a variety of story openings and to categorise them. The sheet reinforces the idea that stories do not have to begin 'at the beginning' – in fact the more exciting ones never do – and do not have to begin 'One day...'. Take this information and awareness back to shared-text work. **Story structure** (page 10) continues with structural elements of texts. The children could use the sheet to check whether their own writing contains these important elements.

Focus on characters (page 11) gives children the opportunity to extract information about characters from texts in a focused way. It also provides an opportunity to distinguish between how characters are portrayed in a story, for example, through dialogue, description and action, and how a reader may feel about them – and why.

Children need to become aware that playscripts are written for performance and that the author has specific intentions, communicated through the text. **Dramatic conventions** (page 12) provides the children with a text extract and a series of questions to highlight the important conventions, such as stage directions, asides and how character can be communicated through words and gestures. Ask the children to perform the text without having considered the conventions. Then discuss the questions on the sheet and ask them to perform it again. Note the differences in performance.

The following four sheets focus on poetry, allowing the children to identify specific aspects of poems but also, within a framework, to be critical of poems they have read. Each activity takes a small aspect of poetry which can be developed through shared-text work in class. **Poems: style and content** (page 13) tackles the difficult distinction between the *style* of a poem (the way in which it is written) and the *content* of a poem (the subject matter). Children often focus only on the subject matter and fail to understand that the effect of the poem comes through its style. This sheet asks children to look at syllable patterns, line length, verse-form, rhyme and what the poets are saying about their subjects. **The poetryometer** (page 14) looks at the *forms* and the *themes* of poems. It is important to distinguish between the *content* of the poem (its subject matter) and what the poet is *really trying to say* by using the subject – its *theme*.

Rhymes and patterns (page 15) takes a poem as a model to show how a pattern can work. The children are asked to find rhyming words; a rhyming dictionary would be useful. Point out to the children that some words have more rhymes than others. Challenge them to find words with the fewest rhymes (*orange* and *silver*). Patterning continues with **Sound poems** (page 16) which also revises onomatopoeia. Here there is no real 'word content'; the story is told completely in nonsense sound words. The children have to be clear about their story first, and then they can invent onomatopoeic words to suit.

Word-play is important for children to discover. Language is fun and authors often play with words to entertain. **Book jokes** (page 17) links with homophones and puns. The answers are: Working with Animals by Sue Keepar (zoo keeper); A Life of Crime by Robin Banks (robbing banks); Avoiding the Flu by I Addit Wonce (I had it once); Learn to Ride a Horse in a Week by Ivor Sorebottom (I've a sore bottom!); Falling Over Cliffs by Eileen Dover (I leaned over); My Life with Santa by Mary Kristmus (Merry Christmas); Animals of the Polar Zones by Ben Gwin (penguin); Collecting Old Furniture by Anne Teek (antique). **More word-play** (page 18) continues this idea and expands the work into more difficult aspects, such as malapropisms. A natural development would be to consider the use of **Literal or figurative language?** (page 22), which provides examples of idioms.

A framework on **Myths and legends** (page 19) is provided to feature key elements and to allow the children to compare myths and legends from a variety of cultures. This is developed further in **Texts from different cultures** (page 23), to enable the children to investigate a range of texts. The answers are: 1. This comes from Scotland and is written in dialect. 2. This comes from the African subcontinent. References to elephants, spiritualism, palmfruit and so on are clues. 3. This comes from the West Indies/Caribbean and is written in dialect. 'Ackee' is a local fruit. 4. This comes from the Indian subcontinent. Scorpions, the god Shiva the monsoon, and flowers such as shiuli are all clues.

Genre game (page 21), allows the children to revise and summarise what they know about various fiction text-types.

A difficult concept for children to grasp is that of the difference between the narrator of a text and the author of a text. This is tackled in **Author or narrator?** (page 20). The first example shows an author. Autobiographies (a person's own life story) are written by the author in the first person, 'I'. The second example is written in the first person, but from the point of view of a cat. This must be narrated, therefore, as in reality cats cannot write or speak! The third example is of a traditional story-telling in the third person. The author is speaking. The final example is a first person narration again.

In **Look closely at a point of view** (page 24), one situation is given and the children are given the opportunity to consider it from a variety of different 'angles'. As with all the activities, a structure is given for the children's writing and talking: what they saw, heard, felt and how they reacted. These elements could be applied to any shared text.

The final activity sheet in this section considers **Literature from the past** (page 25). A passage from *Great Expectations* by Charles Dickens is provided for discussion and to stimulate writing.

Fiction and poetry: writing composition

My reading journal (page 26), **Mapping out a story** (page 27) and **Book rating machine** (page 28) provide generic formats which enable the children to treat difficult aspects of writing about texts in a visual way. Making graphs of text features such as 'tension' or 'excitement' can show young readers where writers position key moments and events; they learn more about the craft of the writer and so can emulate these features in their own work.

Using writers as models can be problematic. Often children just copy the writer's ideas as well as style. The activity sheets **Setting the scene** (page 29) and **New characters** (page 30) use texts as models but give the children the opportunity to extract relevant aspects and put these in their own words. They are not copying the original author, but are seeing how an aspect of writing can work successfully, and then using that awareness in their own writing.

Feelings and moods of a poem (page 31) and **Choosing words and phrases** (page 32) each provides an entire poem for consideration but gives the children a series of questions or choices to make in order that they can see how the poet is using language for specific purposes. Neither of these poems is particularly 'easy' so it is suggested that you read them with a group before you ask the children to work on the sheets. However, both poems are extremely atmospheric and the imagery used is strong and recognisable. An important aspect of such work with poetry is to realise that there may not be a 'right answer' (even with *Fireworks* by James Reeves), but that children's responses, with evidence from the text, can be equally valid. Compare the original with the words the children chose and discuss the differences.

Fireworks

They rise like sudden fiery flowers
That burst upon the night,
Then fall to earth in burning showers
Of crimson, blue, and white.

Like buds too wonderful to name,
Each miracle unfolds,
And catherine-wheels begin to flame
Like whirling marigolds.

Rockets and Roman candles make
An orchard of the sky,
Whence magic trees their petals shake
Upon each gazing eye.

Much of the imagery in poems is created by figurative language; the sheet on **Magic metaphors** (page 33) revises this difficult topic.

You may wish to develop the children's interest in language effects in poetry by using the other poetry sheets in this section: **Using the structure of a poem** (page 36) and **Performance poems** (page 41) provide opportunities for writing a variety of poetry through structured activities. The original lines of the poem featured on page 36 are:

And he lay there on the bottom,
Fanning with his wings of purple,
As above him Hiawatha
In his birch canoe came sailing,
With his fishing line of cedar.

'Take my bait!' cried Hiawatha,
Down into the depths beneath him.
'Take my bait, O Sturgeon, Nahma!
Come up from below the water,
Let us see which is the stronger!'

The remaining sheets in this section offer writing activities covering a range of text-types and features. **Plays and production notes** (page 34) links with an earlier activity on playscripts (page 12). It focuses on plays as performances and asks the children to read a brief extract and make decisions as a stage manager. This could be developed into other curriculum areas, such as making stage sets and costumes in technology. Some children could even provide the lighting for the stage sets. **Your own Robin Hood story** (page 35) uses cards containing features of the Robin Hood legends as a stimulus for the children's own writing. It also provides two 'new ideas' which will involve them in thinking of how the features can be retained while coping with the new problems.

Writing for your audience (page 37) gives the children an insight into 'audience' and how this can change the style of what they are writing. Children often do this automatically when they are speaking and adjust their registers accordingly, but find more difficulty in writing in an appropriate style for an appropriate audience. **Writing from a point of view** (page 38) develops this idea, taking one object and looking at it from a variety of perspectives. In doing so, the children will become aware that a variety of different styles and words will be necessary.

What is happening? (page 39) and **What happens next?** (page 40) consider not only point of view but structure in a story and look at how the sequence of a narrative can affect the reader's response. Both activities require the children to predict what will happen or what they think has happened, based on evidence from pictures.

Non-fiction: reading comprehension

Sports reports (page 42) considers one example of a recounted text and asks the children to identify its features. It is also a useful introduction to fact and opinion. **Instructions for a game** (page 43) considers the important features of instructions and provides the children with a format to help them to write instructions. This could be followed up with sentence-level work on the tenses of verbs, for example: do the instructions use the present tense (*'each player chooses...'*) or the imperative (*'choose...'*)? **To explain how...** (page 44) gives a format which will enable the children to explain a process. An important feature of this kind of non-fiction text is the use of connectives, such as *firstly, ...next, ...so, finally*. They focus on creating a logical order discussing cause and effect.

Two important skills for children to learn so that they can gain the most from non-fiction texts, particularly when they are asked to research, are *skimming* (reading a text to gain a general impression) and *scanning* (reading to find specific information). **A hedgehog calendar** (page 45) and **Family trees** (page 46) provide activities to practise both of these skills. **Finding information** (page 47) is a useful format which enables the children to write about their research issues: what they found difficult as well as where they found the best information. This can be used as an assessment tool to enable both you and the children to find better ways to research, as well as recording exactly what they found out. Children need to be clear about what they are researching before they start. This decision will influence where they look and the kinds of texts from which they take information. They need to be aware of the various text-types and that the same subject can be tackled from many different 'angles' in many different ways and that not all the information they find will be 'the truth'. **Information from different sources** (page 48) shows them this, taking one subject and looking at it in four different ways. **In your own words** (page 49) can help children in their research by providing a visual way of 'writing' difficult, often technical, information from a text – electronic as well as traditional.

The three activities which end this section look at examples of writing for real purposes and how language has to be adjusted to each in a different way. **Letters page** (page 50) asks the children to respond to letters in a magazine, taking into consideration the appropriate style and tone. **Fact and opinion** (page 51) considers the language of promotional leaflets and how these aim to use the words which have been chosen to influence the reader. **Persuasive language** (page 52) provides a format containing words (mostly connectives) associated with persuasive writing, so that the children can structure their arguments.

Non-fiction: writing composition

Writing a recount (page 53) revises the purpose of a recount text (to re-tell information for information or entertainment) and its features. **A personal experience** (page 54) allows the children to put this into practice, using a set of notes provided. You could ask the children to re-write parts of their recounts in a different tense or to re-tell parts of their accounts in a different order. Discuss if they still make their meaning clear.

Different audiences and purposes (page 55) is a game in which the children are given various options for text-type, audience, purpose and subject. Depending on which combination they choose, each will have a different audience and purpose to write about. This will demand their having real awareness of the various language and stylistic features required. This can be used as an assessment activity to check which children have an understanding of text features and which do not.

Writing and testing instructions (page 56) and **Giving instructions** (page 57) provide opportunities for the children to follow a variety of instructions, try them out and then write more instructions using what they have learned.

Making notes (page 58), **Abbreviations track** (page 59) and **Writing up your notes** (page 60) focus on a vital skill: making notes from texts and then being able to communicate the new information in a new form. This is often difficult for children, especially when writing their newly found information in their own words. It is not a valid research outcome for the children merely to copy out of a book or to print out a page from a CD-ROM. Various strategies are suggested on the sheets, from underlining key facts and separating out information by asking key questions, to shortening texts using abbreviations.

An explanation (page 61) shows how an explanation is dependent upon a simple sequence of events. **A letter with a purpose** (page 62) provides source materials from nineteenth-century history to give the children a subject about which to write and a strong stance from which to write. **A leaflet** (page 63) not only considers the stylistic features of the genre but also creates an opportunity for the children to write a commentary on an issue on paper or on screen, setting out and justifying a personal point of view. **Preparing a talk** (page 64) is an extension of this, enabling children to construct an argument in note form to persuade others and to present their case.

Glossary of terms used

alliteration The repetition of a letter or phoneme at the beginning of words in a phrase, for example: *Peter Piper picked a peck of pickled peppers.*
author The person who writes the text. See also **narrator**.
chronology A sequence of events in time, from Cronos, the God of Time.
dialogue A text in which more than one person is speaking. This needs to be punctuated as speech.
discussion text A text which gives **all sides** of an issue. It can be written or spoken.
explanatory text A text which explains a process or answers a question.
figurative language Language which is not literal (factual), for example: **simile** and **metaphor**. Such language is used to create mood or atmosphere.
genre A specific type of writing or other medium of communication, for example: *legend, newspaper story* or *poem.*
haiku A poem of three lines with a specific syllabic pattern: 5, 7, 5. This is an ancient Japanese poetic form.
instructional text A text which gives the reader information to be able to carry out some aim, for example: to make something or to reach a particular place. Instructions use the imperative (command) form of the verb.
literal language Language which is factual, as opposed to **figurative**.
malapropism This occurs when a word is wrongly or unintentionally used in a particular context and it leads to humour, for example: *The ancient Egyptians used to irritate their land* rather than *irrigate their land*. From a character in Sheridan's play *The Rivals* – Mrs Malaprop.
metaphor A comparison, but stronger than a **simile**. Metaphors say something IS something else, for example: *The road was a ribbon of moonlight.*
narrative A text which re-tells events or a story, often in chronological order.
narrator Whoever tells the story in the text. Not necessarily the author.
onomatopoeia The use of words which echo sounds associated with their meaning, for example: *bang, boom, squeak*.
playscript A text written to be performed. The format of a playscript is designed to make actors and directors interpret the text for performance, hence the inclusion of stage directions and clues for more effective performance.
pun a joke which plays upon the idea of homophones and similar-sounding words having two meanings, for example: *Which shellfish is the strongest in the sea?* Answer: *Mussel (muscle).*
quatrain A four-lined poem or verse of a poem which rhymes in a particular sequence, such as alternate lines or in couplets.
recount A text (or part of a text) usually written in the past tense to re-tell for information or entertainment. It uses descriptive language and might include dialogue.
report A non-chronological text usually written in the present tense to describe or classify.
rhyme When words contain the same sound in their last syllables, for example: *go/slow, say/grey*.
scan To look at a text quickly, to locate key words and ideas.
simile A comparison of two things using 'like' or 'as'. This aims to create a picture in the reader's mind.
skim To read a passage to gain an initial overview of the subject matter.

Ways of opening stories

Stories do not have to start 'at the beginning'.

- **Read these opening paragraphs.**
- **Are they from the beginning (B), middle (M) or end (E) of the stories? Write the appropriate letter on each book.**
- **Label each opening paragraph with one of these words:**

dialogue, action **or** description.

'Help! Help!' I screamed as the waters rose around my knees. If only I had listened to my mother that morning.

M | action

My three brothers are very different. You wouldn't think they were related. They are three individuals with only a surname in common.

'It's all your fault,' Raj mumbled. 'You would say that,' I replied. 'You were the one who took the bag.' 'That bag has been a disaster, right from the start...'

The wind was suddenly silent. It was as if the snow-covered body had made it stop. Dark clouds blew across the sky and the sun shone briefly on the man.

I swung the rope around my head, caught hold of the branch and heaved myself from the ground, just as the animal's jaws snapped shut.

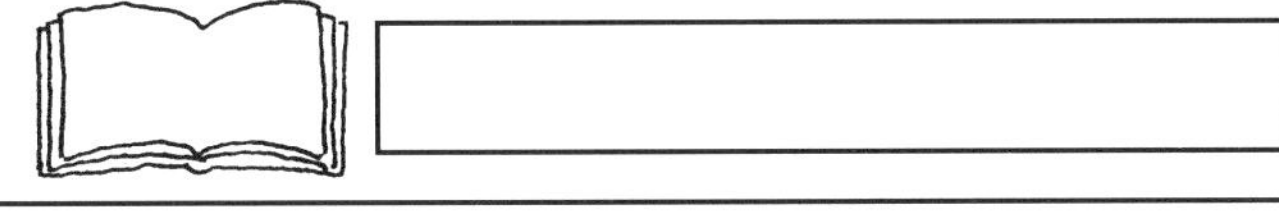

'Just don't come near me... OK? I will scream if you come any closer!' She edged away from the girl whom she thought had been on her side all week.

- **Choose the opening paragraph which you think is the most exciting start to a story.**
- **Continue the story.**

Teachers' note You could discuss the openings of shared texts. Lead the children to an understanding that most stories start with dialogue, description or action. Ask them to find other examples of these kinds of openings and discuss which are the most exciting and why. Introduce the idea of story structure and the fact that stories often begin at places other than the beginning of a narrative.

Story structure

The best stories have a structure – just like a scaffold.

- Use this sheet to identify the important parts of a story.

Title ______________________ Author ______________________

Location	Time	Introduction

Characters	Events in the build-up of the story

How complications develop

Resolution of the story

- Read a story your partner has written.
- Complete the sheet again. Can you find the same features in your partner's story?

Teachers' note You could use the sheet to model the structure of a shared text, explaining to the children such complicated concepts as 'resolution'. Use story structure as a display idea; the children's responses to the various parts of a story could be written on 'bricks' and assembled as an entire 'structure' on the class wall.

Focus on characters

- Use this sheet to help you write about a character.

Name of character ____________________

Book title ____________________

Details of appearance	Details of personality

Examples of what he/she does in the story	What the actions show

Examples of what he/she says	Examples of what others say about him/her

- Use the notes you have made to write a character study.
- Say how you feel about the character. Give evidence from the book to prove your points.

Teachers' note Discuss with the children how it is possible to find out about a character in a book: through dialogue, description and action. Model this, taking a character from a shared text and asking the children to find examples and evidence. Bring out the difference between giving a personal response to a character and providing only information about the character from a text.

Dramatic conventions

When you write a playscript, you must follow the correct style.

The special features of this style are called dramatic conventions**.**

- **Read this script. Think about the answers to the questions.**

What difference does this make to the plot?

Why does the actor need this stage direction?

Why does the playwright give these instructions? How does it add to the mystery and tension?

Why is it necessary for the actors to keep pausing? How does it make you feel?

Ali and Glen are alone in the house.

Glen has just come in. Ali points to the ceiling.

Ali: Listen. (Pause) Can you hear that? (Silence)

Glen: What? (Pause) No, I can't hear anything.

Ali: But it's a noise in the ceiling. Listen. (Pause)

Glen: Mice.

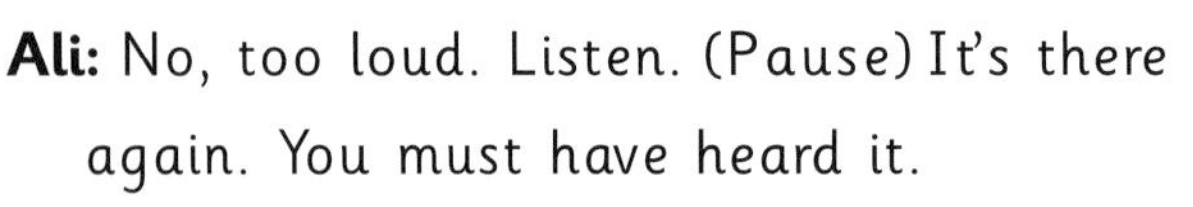

Ali: No, too loud. Listen. (Pause) It's there again. You must have heard it.

Glen: Mice wearing boots then.

(She pretends to hold an ear-trumpet).

What do Glen's actions and words tell you about her character?

How is Ali feeling?

Ali: I've been hearing it since the night we came.

Glen: Rats then.

Ali: No, it's something trying to get out. It's not there all the time.

Glen: You are weird. (Stands on chair and bangs on ceiling.) Clear off! (Knocks three times. Silence. Three knocks back. A moment of silence. They look at each other.)

What information does this give you? How does it make you feel?

How does this action tell you how the characters are feeling?

How does this detail make it more scary?

- **Continue the script, using the dramatic conventions to create tension and a sense of character.**

Teachers' note This activity aims to make children ask themselves questions about how dramatic conventions shape a playscript. They should always be aware through shared text work that plays are written for performance. This also links with writing plays and production notes (see page 34), and gives the children an idea of how to annotate a production script.

Poems: style and content

Poems which seem to be about the same thing are often very different from each other.

- **Read these two poems.**

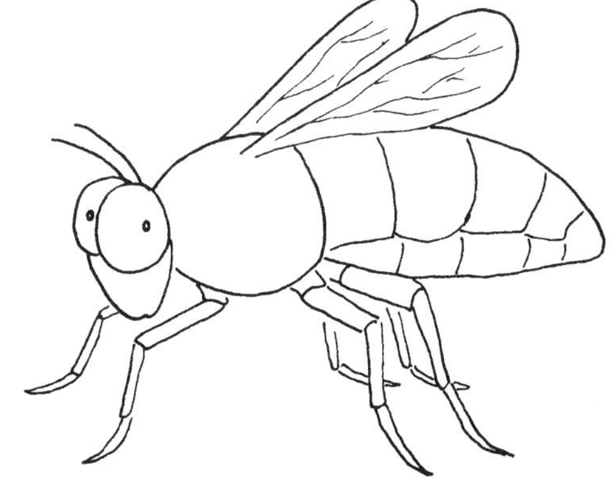

The Fly

How large unto the tiny fly
Must little things appear! –
A rosebud like a feather bed,
Its prickle like a spear;

A dewdrop like a looking-glass,
A hair like golden wire;
The smallest grain of mustard-seed
As fierce as coals of fire.

WALTER DE LA MARE

Fly haiku

On African mouths
Their thin black legs feed and sway.
Silent infection.

- **Complete these two pieces of writing about the poems.**

The poem 'The Fly' is written in two ________.
Each ________ has ________ lines.
The first and third lines have ________ syllables in them. The second and fourth lines have ______ syllables in them. Lines ______ and ______ of each verse rhyme. Four lines which follow this pattern are called a ______________.

The poem 'Fly haiku' is written in ______ lines. The first line contains ________ syllables.
The second line contains __________ syllables. The third line contains __________ syllables.
The poem's lines do not __________.
This kind of poem is called a __________.

- **What is each poet trying to say about a fly?**
  Write your answer, giving evidence from each poem.

Teachers' note In the plenary session you could discuss with the children how the treatment of the subject alters between the two poems. As an additional extension activity, ask the children to find two poems with the same subject in their titles and write about their similarities and differences.

The poetryometer

- Use the poetryometer to organise your ideas about a poem.

Title ______________________ **Author** ______________________

What is the subject of the poem?

What is the poet trying to say?

Verse form (tick)

Written in verses	☐	Haiku	☐
Cinquain	☐	Quatrains	☐
Couplets	☐	Other	☐
Free verse	☐		

Describe the rhythm of the poem. What does it sound like?

How I feel about the poem (out of 10)

5
1 10
disagree agree

It made me happy.
5
1 10
disagree agree

It made me sad.
5
1 10
disagree agree

It made me laugh.
5
1 10
disagree agree

It was scary.
5
1 10
disagree agree

I could imagine the location.
5
1 10
disagree agree

The words were exciting.
5
1 10
disagree agree

What I think of the poem ______________________

____

Reasons ______________________

____

- Use your notes from the poetryometer to write about the poem.
- Include evidence from the poem to support your views.

Teachers' note This sheet allows the children to focus upon forms and themes in poetry. It can be used with any poem. You could model the use of the sheet with a shared text. Distinguish between the content of the poem – its subject matter – and what the poet is really trying to say by the way in which the subject matter is treated.

Rhymes and patterns

- **Read these lines from a nonsense poem about a mysterious person.**
- **Underline the words which rhyme. What pattern do you notice?**

The Akond of Swat

Who, or why, or which, or what,
Is the Akond of SWAT?

Is he tall or short, or dark or fair?
Does he sit on a stool or a sofa or a chair,
or SQUAT,
The Akond of Swat?

EDWARD LEAR

- **Complete this verse. Use the same pattern.**

Who, or why, or which, or what,
Is the Akond of SWAT?

Is he ____________ or ____________, or ____________ or ____________?

Does he stand on a ____________ or a ____________ or a ____________,

or NOT,

The Akond of Swat?

- **Write a verse of your own. Use the same pattern. Change the rhymes.**

The Akond of Rome

Who, or why, or which, or what,
Is the Akond of Rome?

Is he ____

Does he ____

or ____________________

The Akond of Rome?

- **Write two more verses. Change the rhyme sound each time but do not change the pattern.**

Teachers' note The children will find a rhyming dictionary helpful with this activity. You could model the writing of the first verse with them after having drawn out the characteristics of the rhyme scheme and the pattern. In the plenary session the children could discuss words which are difficult to rhyme, such as silver or orange.

Sound poems

Sound poems tell their story entirely through **onomatopoeic** (sound) words.

- **Explain what actions these sound words might describe.**

SPLAT A custard pie in your face! ______

CRUNCH ______

SQUEAL ______

SIZZLE ______

- **Read the sound poem and explain the story behind it. Use the questions to help you.**

The day the washing machine went wrong

Slip slap slip slap slip slap
CLUNK
slip slip slop slip slip
DRIP
EEK!
splish splash splish splash splish
DRIP DRIP GURGLE
Rattle rattle
SPLOOSH
glug glug glug glug

______
______
______
______
______
______

- **Write a four-line sound poem about happenings in a haunted castle.**
- **Ask a partner to tell the story of your sound poem.**

Teachers' note This is an interesting way for children to deal with poetry as there is no real story 'content', although they have to be very aware of story structure and narrative. Groups of children could perform their poems while others guess what they are representing.

Book jokes

Someone has removed the authors' names from all the books in the school library.

- Match the joke authors to the titles.
- Write the correct name on each cover.

Authors

Sue Keepar
Robin Banks
I Addit Wonce
Ivor Sorebottom
Eileen Dover
Mary Kristmus
Ben Gwin
Anne Teek

Avoiding the Flu by

My Life with Santa by

Animals of the Polar Zones by

- Write an explanation of how each joke plays with words and word sounds.

- With a partner, write five more joke titles and authors.

Teachers' note Ask the children to collect jokes which rely on such humour through word-play. There are many links here to word-level work, such as the spelling of homophones and the sounds of various letter patterns. Ensure that the children are aware that word-play is only one way of creating comedy in a text.

More word-play

Puns are jokes which play on words with two meanings.

- **Choose words from the box to complete the jokes.**
- **Explain why the jokes are examples of puns.**

Which shellfish is the strongest in the sea?	Which part of a horse is the most important?	Which is the dullest member of the pig family?
______________	______________	______________

boar   bore   main   mane   muscle   mussel

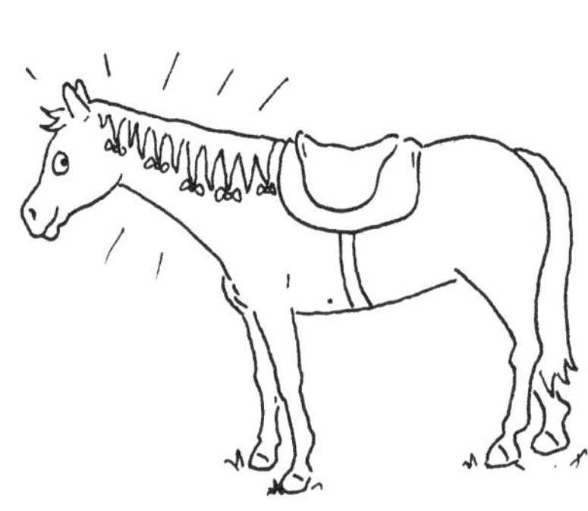

- **A writer can confuse words for comic effect.**
- **What is wrong with these sentences? Why are they funny?**
- **Write your answers.**

Take electrocution lessons to improve your speech.

My friend Raj is the most populous person in the school.

The ancient Egyptians used the Nile to irritate their land.

- **With a partner, write three more jokes which rely on puns.**
- **Write three more expressions with confused words.**

Use reference books.

Teachers' note This work links closely with word-level work, particularly the spelling of homophones (for example, muscle, mussel). Lead the children to an understanding that a writer crafts humour in a text; he or she does not allow it to happen by accident. Ask the children to collect jokes to make an anthology with facing-page explanations, a contents list and an index.

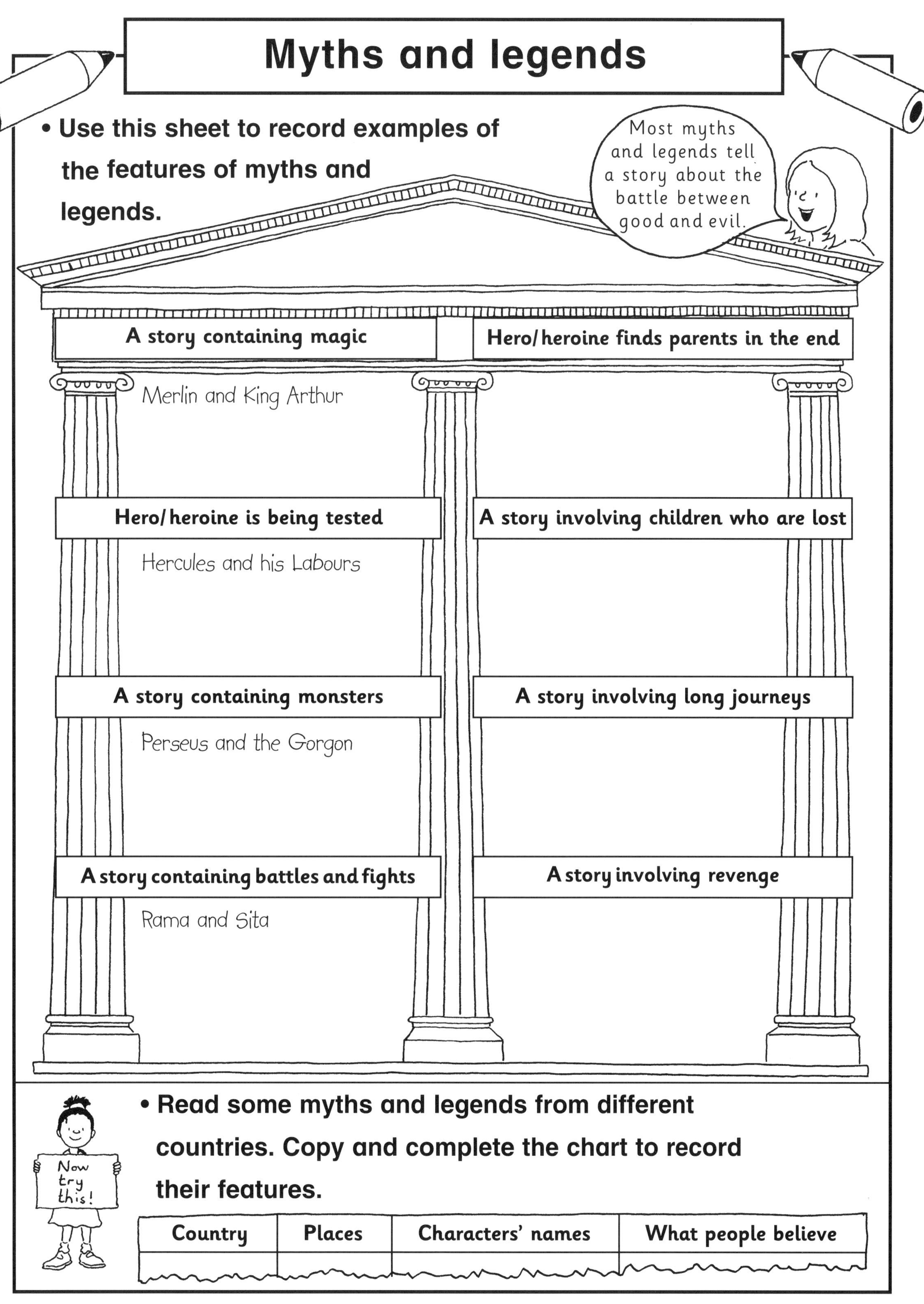

Teachers' note You could model the features of myths and legends through the use of a shared text, such as a Greek myth. Ask the children to provide examples of myths and legends, from Arthurian legend to myths from other cultures, for example, Hindu myths. Analyse their characteristics in the same way. List the myths which use the same stories, such as flood or creation myths.

Author or narrator?

The author is the person who writes the text.

The narrator is whoever tells the story in the text.

- **Decide whether these texts show an author or a narrator. Give reasons for your answers.**

Text	Author or narrator	Reasons with evidence
Tim's autobiography I was born in Wigan but we moved when I was one. I had never been back there until last year. BY TIM		
SuperCat I don't know where I was born but I was left in a box outside the vet's. It was always a mystery how I came by my super-powers to save the cat world. FROM *SuperCat Saves the World*		
Cinderella After the sisters had gone to the ball, she sat down and wept in the cinders. 'I'm so unhappy,' she wailed. Then, behind her, a flash of light illuminated the room. FROM *Fairy Tales*		
Cinders goes out Ladies and Gentlemen. Let me tell you about what really happened to Cinderella at that ball. I am the only person who can tell you because I was actually there. FROM *New Fairy Tales*		

- **Continue one of these stories. Remember to keep to the same style – you are either a narrator or the author.**

Teachers' note The difference in narrative voice between the author and a narrator (someone or something to whom the author gives the story to tell) is a difficult concept for children to grasp. Model with the children various kinds of narrative in shared reading and ask them to identify who is telling the story. The children could try telling stories from different points of view.

Genre game

- Put the picture cards face down and the word cards face up.
- In pairs, take turns to pick a picture card.
- Match it to a word card showing the correct genre.
- Describe the features of that genre, for example, the type of settings and characters.
- Give an example – a book, television programme or film.
- Write down your answers.

Animal stories	Humour	Adventure stories
Mystery	Science fiction	Myths and legends
Horror	Historical fiction	Fantasy

Teachers' note Model how to play the game with the children. You could create a database of the features of various fiction genres and the examples, so that the children could make reference to it and add to it over time. Some of these examples might not be text-based, for example, science fiction may be better known to children from films and television programmes.

Literal or figurative language?

If language is literal, it states a fact.
If language is figurative, it uses a simile or a metaphor.

Similes and metaphors are figures of speech.

- **Write these statements in the correct columns of the chart.**

I'm in a big jam.
I have four cats and two dogs.
I love jam doughnuts.
It rained cats and dogs.
I lost my front-door key.
He threw a stone in the pond.
That's a load of rubbish.
Education is the key to your success.
He left no stone unturned in his search.
Our rubbish is collected every Friday.

Literal language	Figurative language

- **Choose one of the figurative expressions.**
- **Draw a cartoon of it.**
- **Complete the caption.**

Write the expression you have chosen.

____

This is a figurative expression because ______________________________

____

____

- **Write similes (using like or as) about frost, the moon in the sky, noisy children, and a crackling fire.**

Teachers' note As an introduction to this activity, you could look for examples of similes and metaphors in shared texts. Discuss how figurative language is not factual but creates an impression through comparison of ideas. Ask the children to discuss the accuracy of the image created.

Texts from different cultures

These texts come from Africa, India, Scotland and the West Indies.

- **Label each text with the part of the world it comes from.**

1 To a Mouse

Wee, sleekit, cowrin, tim'rous beastie,
O, what a panic's in thy breastie!
Thou need na start awa sae hasty,
Wi' bickering brattle!
ROBERT BURNS

2 Elephant

Elephant, a spirit in the bush,
Elephant who brings death.
He swallows a whole palmfruit
thorns and all.
He tramples down the grass.
ANONYMOUS (TRANS. ULLI BEIER)

3 Linstead Market

Carry me ackee, go
Linstead market.
Not a quatty wut sell,
Carry me ackee, go
Linstead market.
Not a quatty wut sell,
Lard, wat a night, not
a bite,
Wat a Satiday night.
ANONYMOUS

4 Scorpion poem

Scorpion in a ring,
Down by the Shiva temple.
Monsoon had moved him under the sack of rice.
Bringer of death,
We surround him with candles and shiuli flowers.
ANONYMOUS

- **Copy the chart onto a full-size piece of paper. Complete the chart to show how you knew where each text comes from.**

	Language clues	Clues in the detail	Clues in beliefs and attitudes
1			
2			
3			
4			

- **Read other texts from these cultures.**
- **How are they similar to and different from other texts? Write your answers.**

Teachers' note During shared reading, you could investigate a range of texts from different cultures. Ask children to discuss what makes them distinctively different: in language details, references and cultural beliefs and attitudes. Children could display the texts they find on a large class map. Are there any areas where they find few texts? Why could this be?

Look closely at a point of view

Someone's point of view in a story is the way in which he or she sees things. Two people can have different views of the same event.

- **Read this newspaper article.**
- **Imagine you are one of the characters. Tell the story of your day. Write about what you saw, heard and felt, and how you reacted.**

You are Mr Sidney Harbour. Tell the story of your day.

You are another worker at the building site when the accident happens. Tell the story from your point of view.

Daily Shout

Dramatic rescue at building site

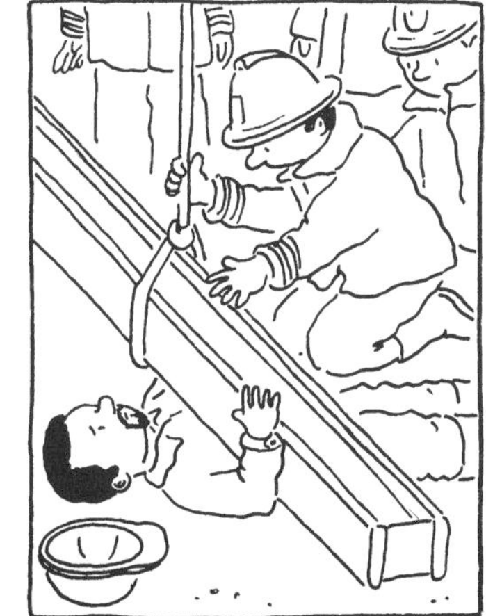

Fire-fighters freed a builder trapped by a steel girder at a building site in central Manchester yesterday.

The builder was Sidney Harbour, aged 33, of Outback Road, Chester. He was taken to hospital and was reported to be in a 'satisfactory condition'.

You are one of the fire-fighters. Tell the story from your point of view.

You are Sidney Harbour's wife. Explain how your husband's accident changed your day.

- **Describe the same event from another character's point of view.**

Teachers' note Model the idea of point of view from a shared text. How would other characters in the situation see the events? Discuss which view is given to the reader as a 'true one'. This links with work on narrators and authors on page 20. You could look at a newspaper article with the children and ask them how many 'points of view stories' they could write from it.

Literature from the past

- **Read the passage from *Great Expectations*, which was written in 1860. This scene describes Pip's thoughts as he meets Miss Havisham for the first time.**
- **Underline words or expressions in the text which tell you that it is from the past.**

I saw that the bride within the bridal dress had withered like the dress, and like the flowers, and had no brightness left but the brightness of her sunken eyes. I saw that the dress had been put upon the rounded figure of a young woman, and that the figure upon which it now hung loose had shrunk to skin and bone. Once, I had been taken to see some ghastly waxwork at the Fair... Once, I had been taken to one of our old marsh churches to see a skeleton in the ashes of a rich dress... Now, waxwork and skeleton seemed to have dark eyes that moved and looked at me...

'Who is it?' said the lady at the table.

'Pip, ma'am.'

'Pip?'

'Mr Pumblechook's boy, ma'am. Come – to play.'

'Come nearer; let me look at you. Come close.'

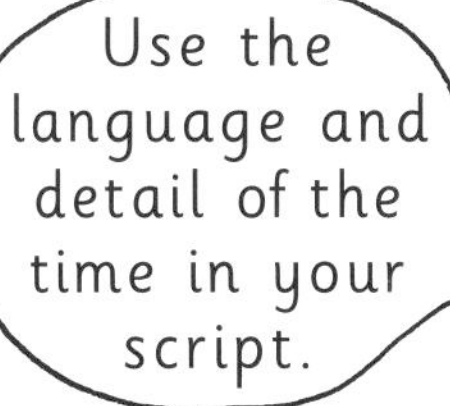

FROM *Great Expectations* BY CHARLES DICKENS

- **Imagine that *Great Expectations* is being made into a television serial. Write the script for this scene. Begin by describing the setting and the characters.**

Use the language and detail of the time in your script.

Setting: Miss Havisham's house. A room full of cobwebs.

Characters:

- **Continue your script for the scene. What do you think will happen?**

Teachers' note This sheet serves as an introduction to the challenge and appeal of older literature. Children will not be able to read all of the original, but abridged versions are available. Discuss how books can be adapted for television serialisation. This novel has had many versions made for film and television. You could show the children this scene and compare it with their scripts.

My reading journal

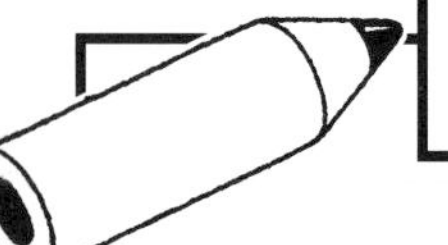

- **Use this page to help you write your reading journal.**

Name ____________________

Class ____________________ **Date** ____________________

Title ____________________

Author ____________________

Fiction/Non-fiction ____________________

What is the book about?

For a fiction book, list some of the characters.

What are the characters like? Give evidence.

For a non-fiction book, say if the information was easy or difficult to understand. Give reasons.

Now write your final thoughts about the book.

- **Use your notes to write a longer piece about the book.**

Teachers' note Discuss the reasons for writing a reading journal and why the various sections of the journal are important, for example: why is it important to put the date? The children should be made aware of the features of the journal and the kind and quality of information required. Each child could produce a reading journal for the books read for a class topic.

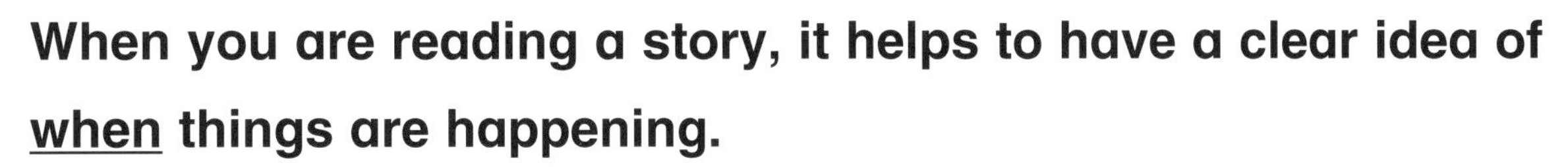

Mapping out a story

When you are reading a story, it helps to have a clear idea of when things are happening.

- Fill in the chart to show when the important events happen in a story.

Title ______________________ Author ______________________

Page or chapter	Event	The time in the story (the hour, day or year)

- Map out the excitement level of the story on this graph.
- Where do the exciting parts come?

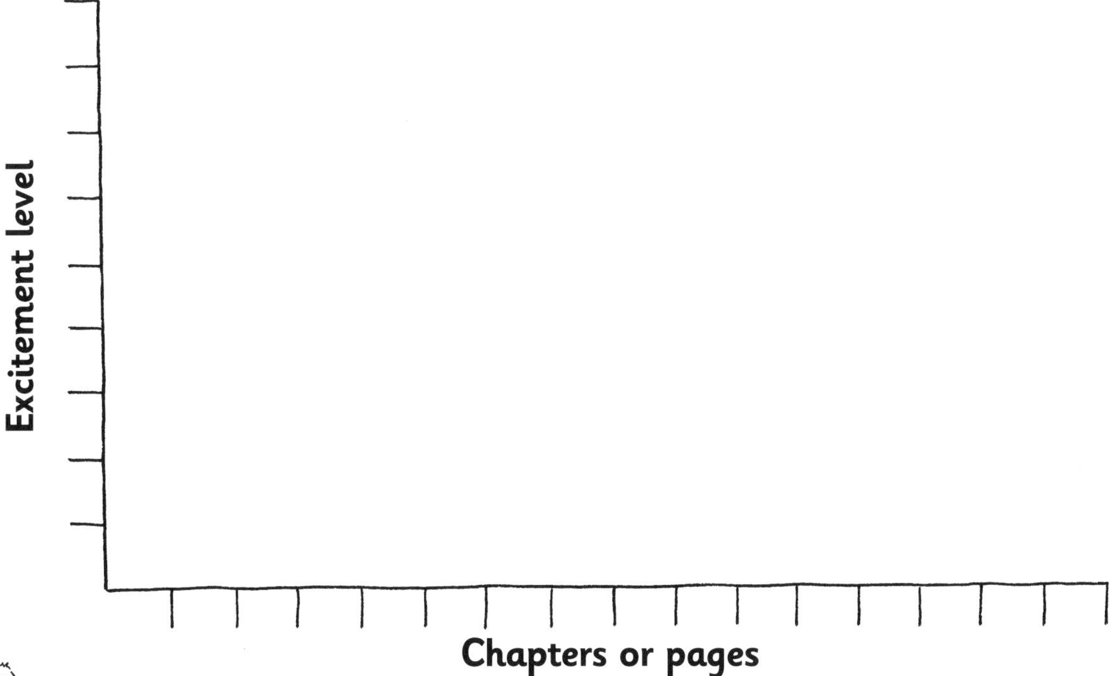

- Use a similar graph to map out the tension level in a different text. Where in the story does most tension occur?

Teachers' note Introduce the idea of mapping out certain ideas in a text. This ensures that children can visually represent important features of text-level work. Graphs show when the 'high' and 'low' points occur in story structure – in this case, of excitement or tension. You could display all the graphs to emphasise where tension or excitement usually occurs in a narrative.

Book rating machine

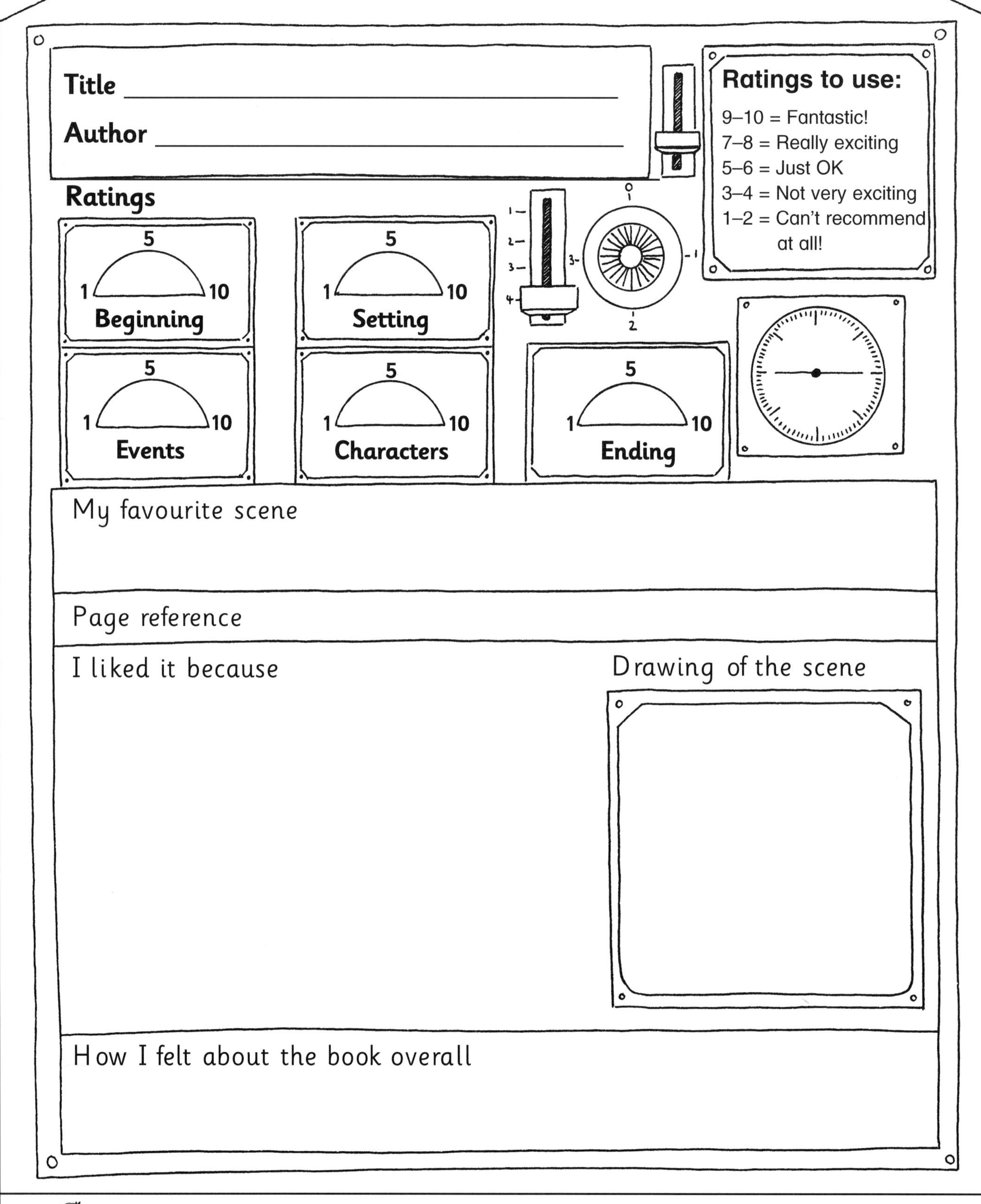

- **Find somebody who read the same book but felt differently about it.**
- **Compare your ratings. Discuss your differences.**

Teachers' note This is another way of mapping out texts (see also page 27). Children are asked to consider the various elements of story structure in a fun way. In the extension activity they should focus on their areas of interest (or lack of interest) and explain why they felt the way they did. At all times, they should be learning to back their assertions with evidence from the text.

Setting the scene

- **Read this extract from a poem. It sets the scene.**

'Is there anybody there?' said the Traveller,
Knocking on the moonlit door;
And his horse in the silence champed the grasses
Of the forest's ferny floor:
And a bird flew up out of the turret,
Above the Traveller's head:
And he smote* upon the door again a second time;
'Is there anybody there?' he said.

*banged

FROM *The Listeners* BY WALTER DE LA MARE

- **Fill in the chart to show what you have learned about the scene.**

Question	What I learned	Evidence
What time of day is it?		
Where is this happening?		
How many people are around?		
Is it a town or a country scene?		
What kind of buildings are around?		
What animals are in the scene?		
What sort of noises are there?		

- **Draw your impression of the scene.**
- **Write what you think happens next. Use details from the scene in your story.**

Teachers' note The children need to be aware of how an author creates a scene through his or her use of detail before they can write a scene in the style of that author. As an introduction to the activity you could ask the children to point to a couple of details. Try blanking out or changing details; what is the effect on the impression of the scene?

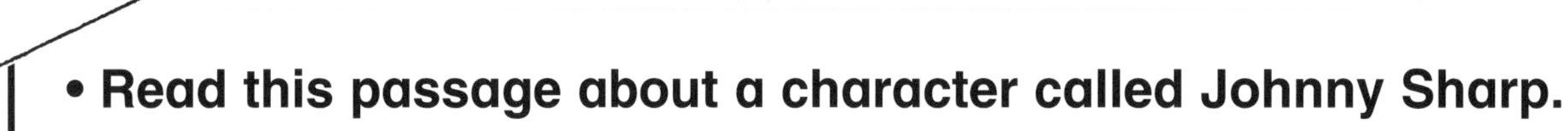

New characters

- **Read this passage about a character called Johnny Sharp.**
- **Underline the words and phrases which tell you that the author does not like him.**

Johnny Sharp wore a grey homburg hat, rather on the back of his head and cocked sideways, with the brim turned down in front. He had a foxy sort of face – narrow eyes, long thin nose, long thin lips; he grinned a lot, showing his bad teeth and a gold-stopped one on the left of his upper jaw. He had a loud check suit with padded shoulders, and a perfectly ghastly tie with large patterns on it... he had two flashy rings on his right hand... he was a narrow, wriggling sort of chap, from top to bottom; like a dressed-up eel. Or a snake.

FROM *The Otterbury Incident* BY C DAY-LEWIS

- **Complete the chart to describe Johnny Sharp.**

Feature of character	Evidence	Impression of character
Clothes he wears		
The way he wears them		
Eyes, nose and lips		
Jewellery he wears		

- **The author compares Johnny Sharp to two creatures at the end of this passage. How does this make you feel about the character?**

____

____

- **Re-write the description. Change the detail to make Johnny Sharp seem pleasant and likeable.**

Teachers' note The children need to be aware of how an author creates character through his or her use of detail before they can write a scene in the style of that author. As an introduction to the activity you could ask the children to point to a couple of details. Do the details make the children like or dislike the person? Why? They could draw their impressions of the character and compare results.

Feelings and moods of a poem

This poem describes a foggy scene in Victorian London.

- **Read the poem and answer the questions.**

1. How do you move if you crawl? What does this verb say about the way in which the bus moves?

2. How does the repetition of this colour throughout the poem add to the atmosphere?

3. The poet uses a simile of a butterfly. How would this insect move on the ground?

4. How big are midges? What does this tell you about what the poet can see?

5. Why is the wharf by the river shadowy ?

6. Is a rod hard or soft? Is it straight or curved? What does this tell you about the poet's view of the river?

7. What does this word mean? How does it describe the river?

8. What colour is this? How does it make you feel about the water?

An omnibus across the bridge
Crawls like a yellow butterfly,
And, here and there, a passer-by
Shows like a little restless midge.

Big barges full of yellow hay
Are moved across the shadowy wharf,
And, like a yellow silken scarf,
The thick fog hangs along the quay.

The yellow leaves begin to fade
And flutter from the Temple elms,
And at my feet the pale green Thames
Lies like a rod of rippled jade.

OSCAR WILDE

Use a dictionary.

1. When you crawl, you move slowly. This is how the bus is moving in the fog.
2.

- **Write a paragraph describing how the poem makes you feel about the scene, and why.**

Teachers' note In the plenary session you could discuss with the children how words and images create the slow, langorous mood of the poem. Link this with sentence-level work to discuss the impact of verbs such as 'crawls' and 'flutter'. Ask them to comment on the colours used – particularly yellow – and how these add to the feeling of the poem.

Choosing words and phrases

- **Read the poem. Write in each box the word that you think is best for the space.**

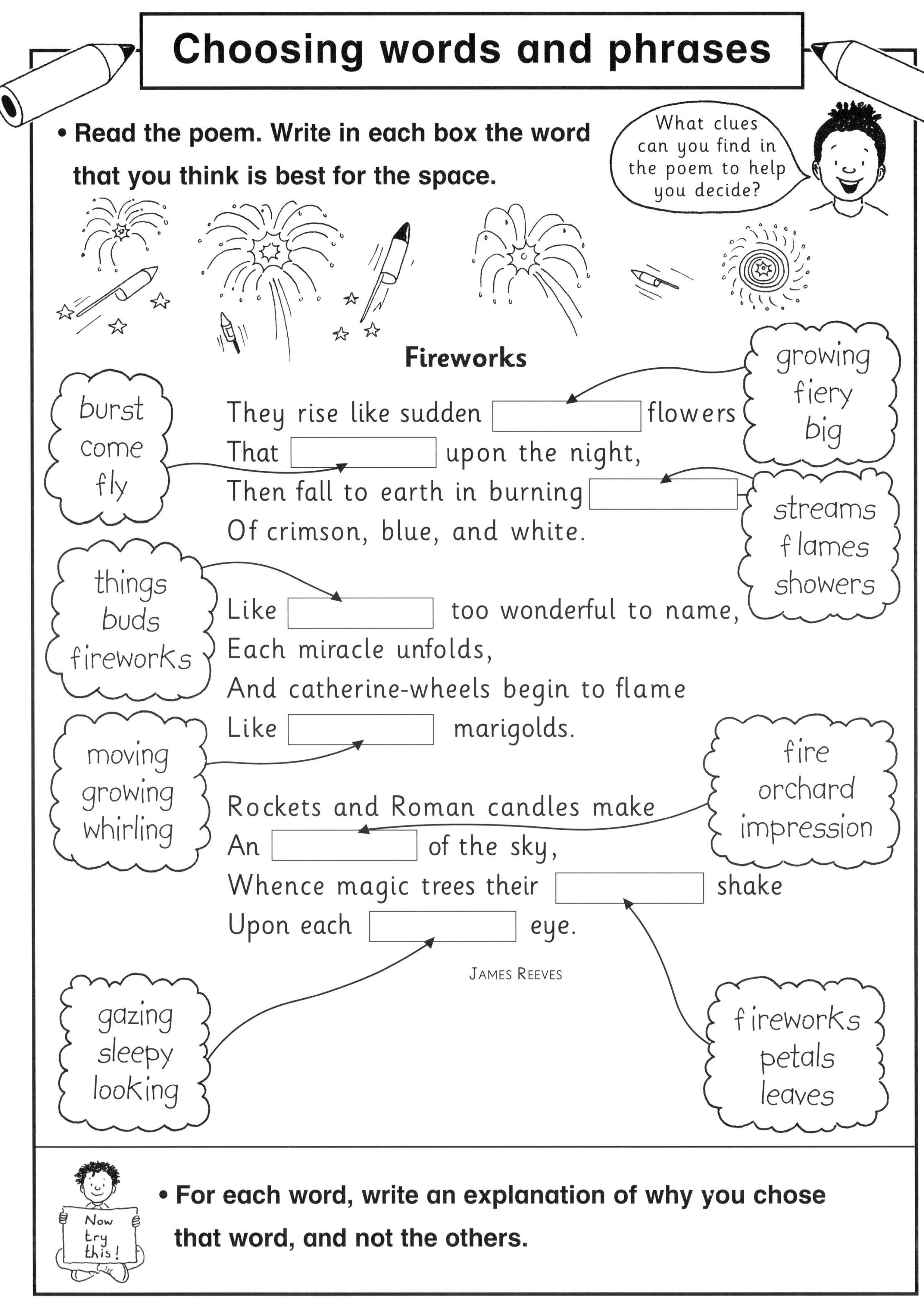

Fireworks

They rise like sudden ______ flowers
That ______ upon the night,
Then fall to earth in burning ______
Of crimson, blue, and white.

Like ______ too wonderful to name,
Each miracle unfolds,
And catherine-wheels begin to flame
Like ______ marigolds.

Rockets and Roman candles make
An ______ of the sky,
Whence magic trees their ______ shake
Upon each ______ eye.

JAMES REEVES

- **For each word, write an explanation of why you chose that word, and not the others.**

Teachers' note You could explain to the children that the object of discussing a poem in this way is not to come to a 'correct answer' but for the children to give their reasons as to why certain words or phrases are better than others within a particular context. You could make a display of useful expressions to use when talking or writing about poems.

Magic metaphors

Be a metaphor magician – change the similes into metaphors!

- **Underline the simile in each sentence.**
- **Re-write the simile as a metaphor.**
- **Circle the words which you have used metaphorically.**

Example: The road was <u>like a ribbon of moonlight</u>.

The road was a (ribbon) of moonlight.

1. The fog curled like a cat around the tree.

2. The wind grabbed the leaves like hands.

3. He moved like a bulldozer through the crowd.

4. The dead tree was like a skeleton outlined on the hilltop.

Now try this!

- **Look through a book to find five metaphors.**
- **Change them into similes, using**  like **or** as.

Teachers' note The concept of figurative language is difficult for many children to grasp. Collect similes and ask children to add to the lists. Focus on the 'like' or 'as' words through underlining. Model with them how you can transform a simile into a metaphor; sometimes it is just a matter of changing the verb form. This also links with work on literal and figurative language (see page 22).

Plays and production notes

- **Read this extract from a playscript about the Greek myth of *Heracles*.**
- **Write notes for a production.**

Heracles, the Greek hero, needs the three Golden Apples from the tree in Paradise. Only Atlas, who holds up the sky, can help him.

Atlas: (holding up the sky on his shoulders) Oh! I am so tired. I long to walk around the Earth again.
Heracles: (putting down his weapons and flattering the god) You can, great god. Just walk into the garden and fetch me the apples. I will hold up the skies for you.
Atlas: (moving the weight on his shoulders) But first you need to kill the dragon at the foot of the tree. (Heracles fits a golden arrow to his beautiful bow, aims and fires. There is a scream and the creature hobbles away to die.)
Heracles: (taking the weight of the skies) This is so heavy. Atlas, go and fetch the apples. I will be glad to get rid of this burden.
Atlas: (walking away and whispering to himself) I will get the apples, but I will never take that weight again! You are a fool, Heracles.

- **Take a playscript you are reading in class.**
- **With a partner, write notes for a production.**

Teachers' note Link this work with page 12 on dramatic conventions, as these are an important part of perceiving playscripts as meant for production. The children could make models of the stage sets in technology and design and make masks and costumes for a performance.

Your own Robin Hood story

• Plan your own story about Robin Hood. Use the pictures to help you.

• Choose one of these new ideas to include in your story.

New idea 1	Robin Hood is badly injured in an accident.
New idea 2	Robin Hood's son joins the villains to fight against his father.

• Write how the new idea changes your plan of the story. What has to happen to make your story turn out happily in the end?

• Now write your story.

Teachers' note To introduce the activity you could discuss myths and legends about Robin Hood with the children. Allow the children to discuss the impact each new story scenario would have and how the story would have to be structured in order for an appropriate ending to emerge.

Using the structure of a poem

- **Read the lines of poetry about a giant fish. Hiawatha, a Native American, is trying to catch the fish.**
- **Tap out the rhythm. What does it remind you of?** ________________

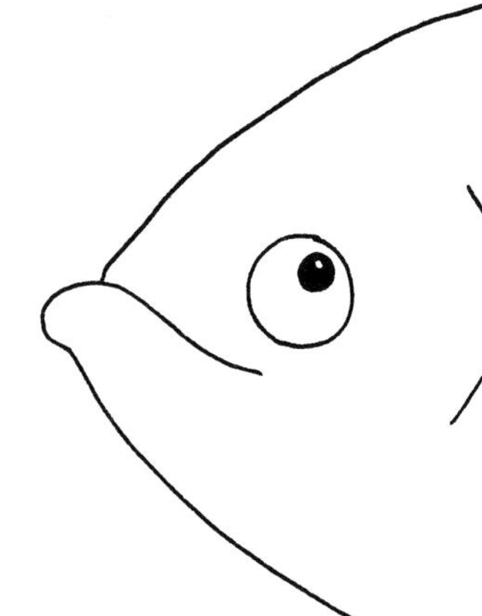

There he lay in all his armour;
On each side a shield to guard him,
Plate of bone upon his forehead,
Down his sides and back and shoulders
Plates of bone with spines projecting!
Painted was he with his war-paints,
Stripes of yellow, red and azure,
Spots of brown and spots of sable...

FROM *Hiawatha* BY HENRY WADSWORTH LONGFELLOW

- **Follow the rhythm and pattern of the poem. Complete these lines in your own words:**

And he lay there on the ________________,
Fanning with his fins of ________________,
As ________________ him Hiawatha
In his ________________ canoe came sailing,
With his fishing line of ________________.

Count out the syllables. Is there a pattern?

- **Write four of your own lines. Describe how Hiawatha battled with the giant fish. Use the same rhythm and pattern.**

'Take my bait!' cried Hiawatha,

____

____

____

____

- **Find a poem in which the rhythm shows an action, for example, riding a horse.**
- **Write lines of your own following the pattern.**

Teachers' note Model the poem with the children until they realise that the rhythm is imitating Native American drumming. This brings its own constraints when writing in the same style, as the children must follow a syllabic pattern. Ask them to count the syllables of each line and establish the pattern. They should then check the new words they have chosen against this pattern.

Writing for your audience

Different ways of writing suit different audiences.

- Look at the picture. Jack is in trouble at school.
- Imagine you are Jack. Write three different descriptions of what happened.

1. To your best friend

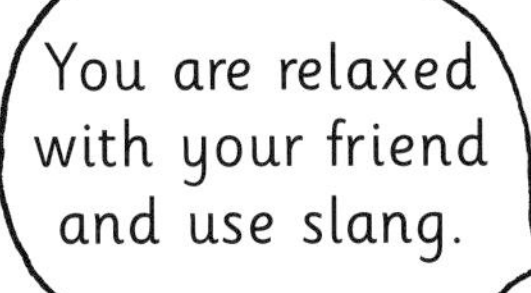

2. To your parents

3. To your headteacher

- Think of something which has happened in school recently. Write two versions of the event: as the headteacher informing the Governors, and as yourself telling a friend in the playground. How are the versions different?

Teachers' note This activity links with sentence-level work on standard English. Discuss with the children how a skilled speaker will automatically adjust his or her speech as the situation demands. You could ask the children to write about situations when the level of formality is inappropriate to the situation. This can lead to comic as well as serious situations.

Writing from a point of view

We all look at things in different ways.

- **Make notes to explain how each of these people views a cow.**

A city-lover

A scientist

A meat-eater

Jack (from *Jack and the Beanstalk*)

- **Write four descriptions of the cow to show each different point of view.**

Teachers' note To introduce the activity you could show the children a picture and establish what is actually in it. Then ask them to imagine they are a different person and look at the scene again. How does the perception of it change? You could display the different pieces of writing around the object which inspired them, to show the variety of approaches.

What is happening?

- **Look at the picture. Note down what you think is happening.**

- **Answer these questions. Do they make you change your mind?**

1. Is the boy being held back or is he being picked on?

____

____

2. Is the boy on the left punching him or trying to help him?

____

____

3. Is the boy on the right being attacked, is he the attacker or is he trying to help?

____

____

4. Suppose a television camera was just outside the picture. How would this change your view?

____

____

- **Write what you believe is happening in the picture.**
- **Write what you think happened leading up to the event in the picture.**

Teachers' note This is an opportunity to revise work on point of view and also on how images can be misleading. When dealing with images in a shared text, for example, the cover of a book, it is useful to discuss with the children what they think has happened and will happen in the story. What clues give them that particular impression? See the work on sequencing on page 40.

What happens next?

- **Put the pictures in the correct sequence to tell the story.**
- **Write the story so far.**
  Include speech in the story.

- **Predict what might happen next and write it.**

Teachers' note When you are discussing shared texts, challenge the children to predict what will happen next, but always ask them for evidence to support their assertions. Ask the children to write alternative endings to well-known stories. You could display the stories to show how the same structure and detail can produce many different endings, not necessarily 'happily ever after'.

Performance poems

- **Read this poem, which was written to be performed.**
- **What actions would you use to perform it? Write your ideas.**
- **Underline the words which you would stress.**

A Rainy Day

When Becky woke up she jumped out of bed,
Had a big yawn,
Scratched her head,
Opened her window, looked out and said,
'Oh bother the rain!'
Got back into bed
And went to sleep again.

When Becky woke up she jumped out of bed,
Had a big yawn,
Scratched her head,
Rubbed her eyes, wiggled her toes,
Found her hanky, blew her nose,
Opened her window, looked out and said,
'Oh bother the rain!'
Got back into bed
And went to sleep again.

DAVID ORME

- **Make up the next verse, following the same pattern.**

When Becky woke up

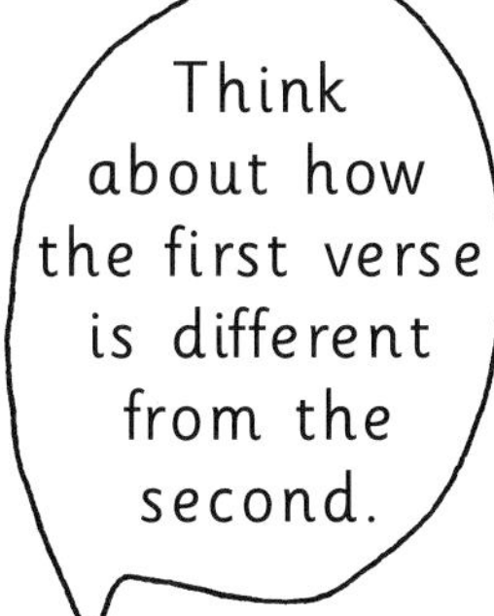

- **With a partner, find another performance poem.**
- **Decide which words and phrases need to be emphasised.**
- **Make a list of actions for the poem. Perform it!**

Teachers' note You could model with the children how the poem can be more exciting if certain parts are stressed and actions are performed. Ask them to decide which parts need to be spoken in a different way and why. Use anthologies in the class to find poems which could be performed, rather than just read. Make a separate anthology of these poems and use it as a shared text.

Sports reports

- Read the football match report.
- Draw a line from each label to the correct place in the report.
- Underline each feature in the text in a different colour.

Smithfield Rovers 2 Magnus United 1

Supporters at Saturday's match must have thought it was worth standing in the rain to see such an exciting match.

First Disney opened the scoring for Rovers after only seven minutes, even with his leg in plaster.

Then he was fouled by Smith, who brought him to the ground with his walking stick. Fortunately Disney was not injured, and slotted his penalty kick into the back of the net.

Next, the Rovers' goalkeeper left his position to talk to his girlfriend, and the ball shot past him. Jones, the scorer, celebrated with a 'nice cup of tea' at half-time.

But even more exciting after half-time was the appearance of Disney's mother. She appeared on the pitch with his clean shirt insisting he change while she washed the dirty one.

Finally, the referee blew his whistle and the players left for tea. The home team always had the better of the visitors. But what a great game it had been for the pensioners.

Think about why reports like this have to follow a sequence of events in the right order.

An introduction to set the scene

The first event

Some detail about the first event

The second event

Some detail about the second event

Using connectives to suggest time passing

A conclusion

- **Write your own sports report of a match you have seen.**
- **Make sure you use the features on this page.**

Teachers' note Model with the children characteristics of recounted texts. See also pages 53 and 54 for further approaches. Writing sports reports can also start a discussion of what is fact and what is opinion. Are the children stating the facts or are they allowing their preferences to change the language and narrative stance they are adopting?

Instructions for a game

• Use this sheet to write instructions for a game.

Title of game ______________________

A game for __________ players.

Object of the game ______________________

Equipment needed

1. ______________________ Diagram

____

____

____

2. ______________________ Diagram

____

____

____

3. ______________________ Diagram

____

____

____

4. ______________________ Diagram

____

____

____

Now try this!

• **Underline the verbs in your instructions. What do you notice about the tense?**

Teachers' note In the plenary session you could discuss how instructions can be written in the simple present tense, for example: 'Each player chooses...' or in the imperative – 'Choose...'. Discuss how valuable the visuals are. What happens if the instructions are not written in chronological order? See also pages 56–57 for different kinds of instructions.

To explain how...

- Use this sheet to help you explain how a simple process works.
- Write the title of your explanation in the centre.

1. I am going to explain how...

2. Firstly...

3. The result of this is...

4. After that...

5. So, the result of that is...

6. Next...

7. Then...

8. So, finally...

How ____________

- Choose another simple process.
- Write an explanation of it, using the ideas on this sheet.

Teachers' note The key feature of explanations which should be brought out in shared reading and writing is the importance of a series of logical steps. The children could try following the explanation they write on this page in a different order. What is the effect? Note that this sheet is causal – that is, the connectives used suggest cause and effect in the explanation.

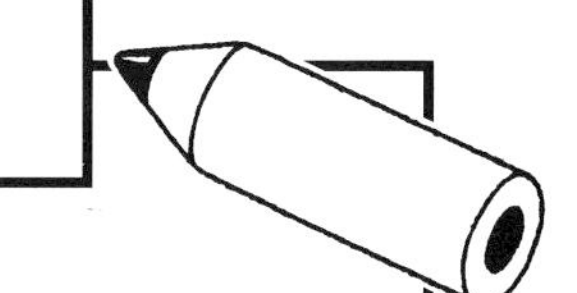

A hedgehog calendar

• **Look at the calendar diagram about hedgehogs.**

January Hibernating – using up fat	**February** Still hibernating – fat almost used up 	**March** Weather warmer – comes out 	**April** Feeding – to build up fat
May Looking for a mate to start a family	**June** 4–5 babies born – no spines – feed on milk 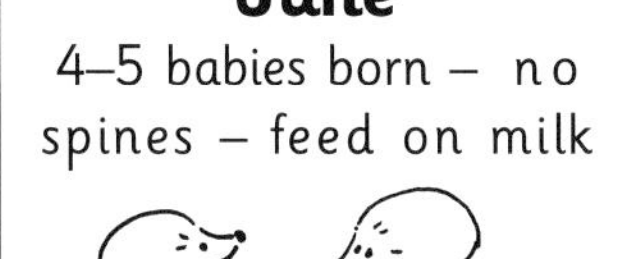	**July** Family starts to explore 	**August** Family feeds separately – food is plentiful – build up fat
September Another litter of 4–5 babies	**October** Building nests from leaves and twigs 	**November** Start hibernating – enough fat reserves	**December** Hibernating 

• **Write the answers to these questions.**

1. How many baby hedgehogs are born in each family in a year?

2. For how many months a year do hedgehogs hibernate?

3. What do hedgehogs use to build their nests? Why do they need to have a warm nest?

4. Why is it important for hedgehogs to build up their fat reserves?

• **Write four more questions for a partner to answer.**

• **Draw your own calendar diagram. It could be about your school year or special festivals you attend.**

Teachers' note When dealing with non-fiction texts, you could ask children to note down design features which enable them to read information more easily, for example: diagrams, bullet points and sub-headings. Discuss whether it is easier to find information from diagrams like this or from paragraphs of text and why.

Family trees

• **Pick out information from the passage to complete the family tree.**

Gods of Ancient Greece

Uranus, the god of the Heavens married Gaea, the goddess of the Earth. They had three children – the Titans: Cronos, Phoebe and Oceanus. Cronos married Rhea and their children were Hestia (the goddess of the fire and hearth), Hades (who was the god of the kingdom of the dead), Poseidon (the god of earthquakes and the sea), Zeus (the King of the gods) and Demeter (the goddess of the harvest). The goddess of wisdom, Athena, was the child of Zeus and Hera, as were Ares and Hebe.

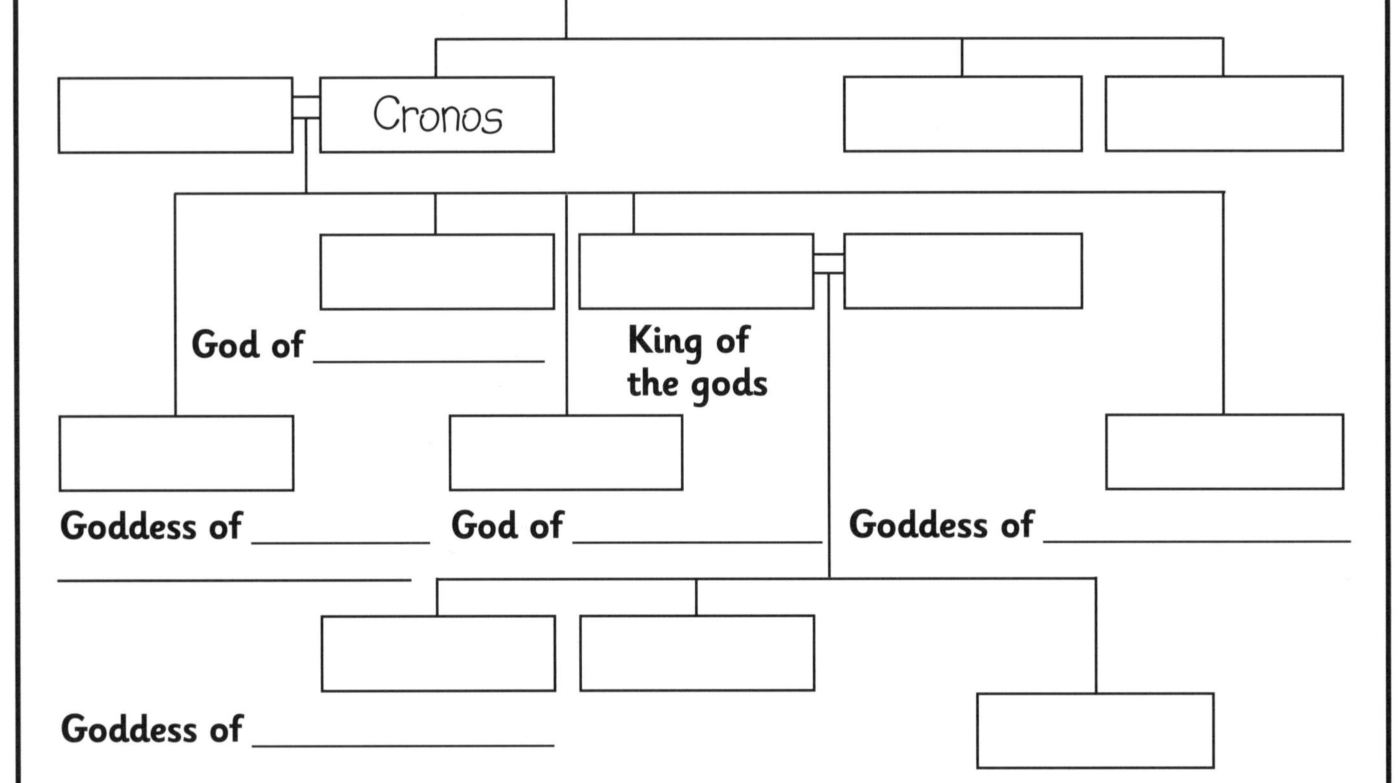

• **Draw a family tree for your family. Give it to a partner and ask him or her to write a paragraph about your family.**

Teachers' note This is an exercise in 'scanning' a text, that is, reading to find specific information. You could give the children diagrams, formats or charts to complete in order to guide their note-taking. Display the various formats and ask the children which formats make information-gathering easier.

Finding information

- Think about how you have found information that you needed. Complete the chart.

What I needed to find out:

Where I went to find the information:

The most helpful books were:

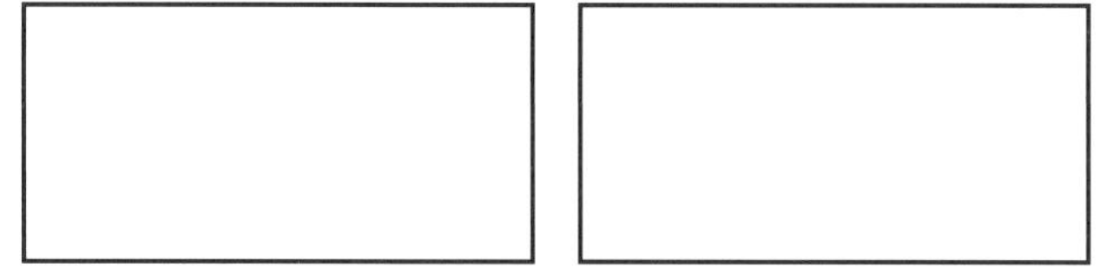
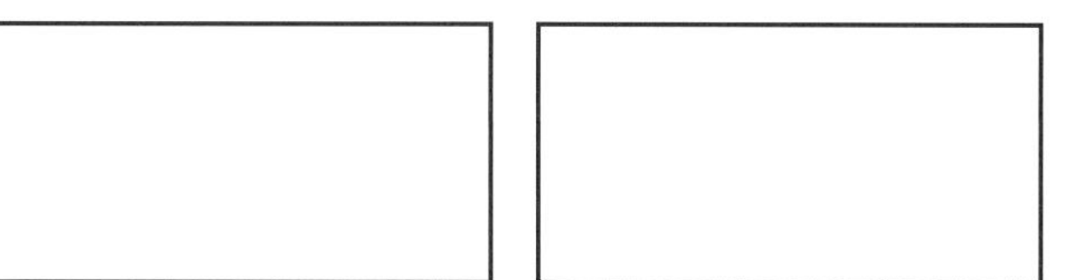

I used: a glossary ☐ an index ☐ a booklist ☐ sub-headings ☐

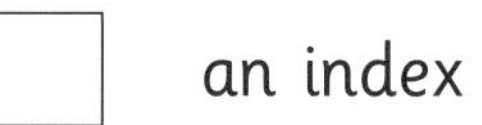

The most helpful CD-ROMs were:

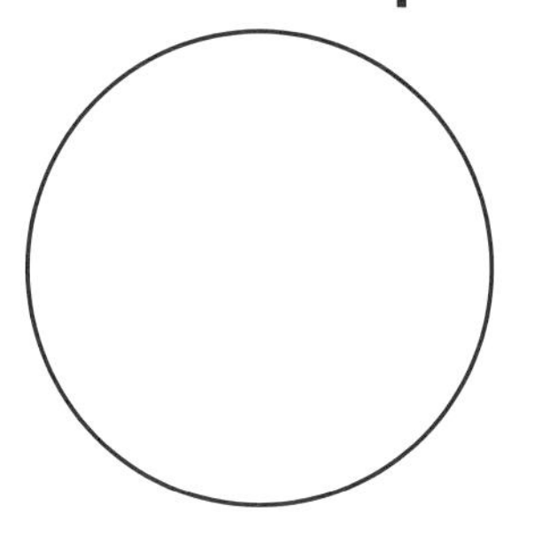
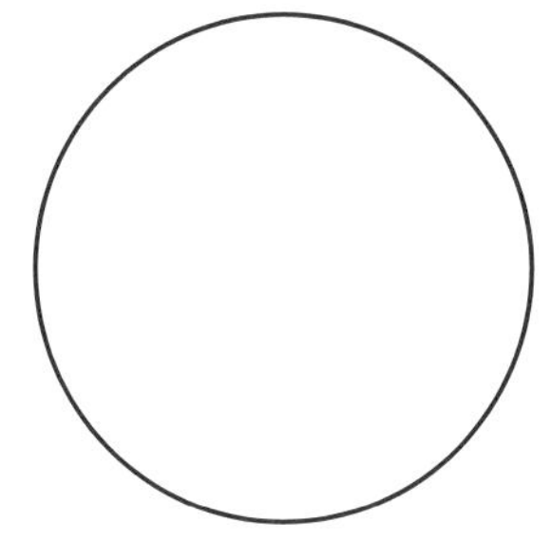
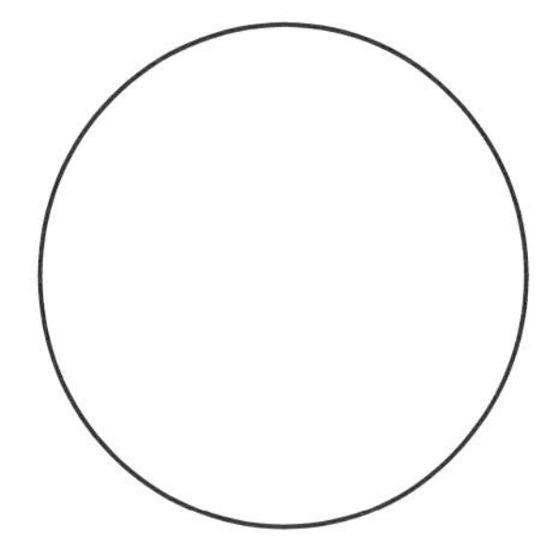
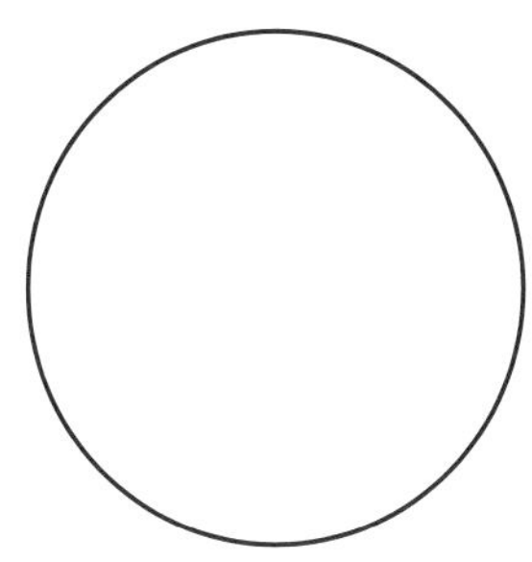

Problems which made it difficult for me to find out information were:

I shared what I found out with:

- Make a list of questions to which you want to find the answers. Copy and complete the chart.

Question	What I need to find out	Where I shall look for information

Teachers' note This page gives the children a chance to reflect on the work they have done and serves as a focus for future research. You could make a collection of the children's sheets on the same subject of research. Ask the children to note what makes their research difficult. Ensure that they know how to use indexes, glossaries and booklists.

Information from different sources

- **Join each passage to its label.**

1. In the USA, 75% of chewing gum is eaten by 10% of the population. Americans chew enough gum to make a single piece 5 million miles long.

2. It was Alexander the Great's troops who were first recorded chewing wild mint. Chewing gum was invented by a Mr Adams who could not make the sap of a South American tree into synthetic rubber, so he tried eating it.

3. To make chewing gum: Take materials for a gum base (completely synthetic). Mix with sugar, corn syrup, flavourings and softeners.

4. New! Chewy-gum-gum THE most natural gum in the world. Recommended by ALL dentists. Chewing actually helps your teeth! Splendiferously chewy! HURRY – special offers end soon!

Instructional text

Informative text

Persuasive text

A recount text

- **Complete the chart.**

Text	What is it trying to do?	Where might it be from?
1		
2		
3		
4		

- **Write questions based on the information on this page. Underline the most important statements to help you.**

Teachers' note Discuss with the children how non-fiction texts on the same subject can have different aims. This should be clear to them before they start searching for information in a text. You could make a collection of different text-types on one common subject. Label and display them.

In your own words

Non-fiction texts sometimes contain technical words which can be difficult to understand.

Use a dictionary.

- **Read this passage.**

Plastics

Have you ever wondered why some plastics melt and others do not? For example, if a yogurt pot comes near a flame it will change shape. A light-bulb holder is also made of plastic but it does not change shape, even though the light-bulb gets hot. A yogurt pot is made of thermoplastic material ('therm' means 'heat'). This means it will soften in the heat and then go harder again when it cools. The light-bulb holder is made of thermosetting plastic. This cannot be made softer by heating up. Once it is hard, it stays hard.

- **Complete the labels on the diagrams.**

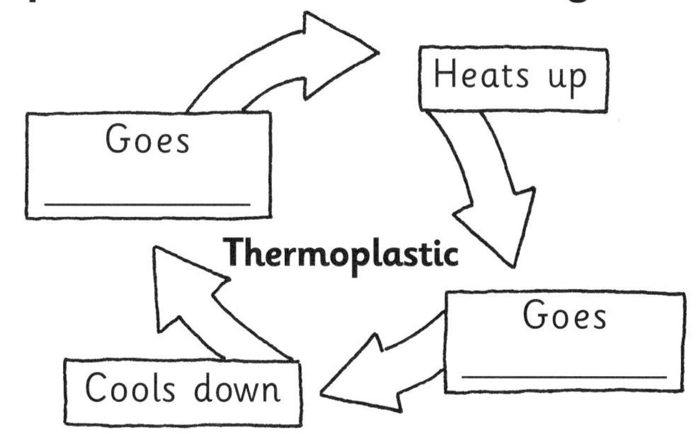

Heats up

Thermosetting plastic

Stays ______

- **Explain the two kinds of plastic in your own words.**

____

____

____

____

____

____

- **Draw a similar diagram to show a simple process.**
- **Explain the process in your own words.**

Teachers' note In this activity, looking at the difficult words away from the passage in diagrammatic form enables the children to see the words in context more easily. You could practise using dictionaries with the children to find the meanings of difficult words.

Letters page

- **Read this letter to a magazine vet and the reply.**

Dear Vet,
My hamster is called Hamlet. She was really tame until she had babies. Now she goes for me if I put my hand in her cage or if I try to pick up one of her babies. Can you tell me how to tame her again?
TINA FROM TAMWORTH

Well, Tina. It's quite normal for your hamster to protect her babies. In the wild they are solitary creatures. How would you like it if a huge hand one hundred times your size tried to come near you? Leave her alone until her babies are old enough. Handle her very gently to begin with. I am sure you will get on better with her. Good luck!

- **Research the answers to the questions in this letter.**
- **Write a reply.**

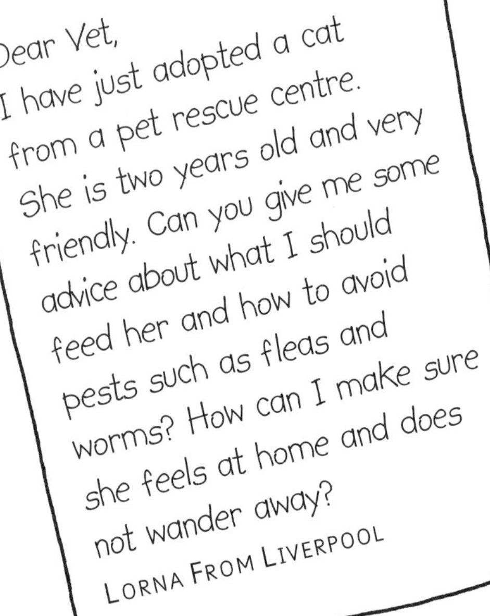

Dear Vet,
I have just adopted a cat from a pet rescue centre. She is two years old and very friendly. Can you give me some advice about what I should feed her and how to avoid pests such as fleas and worms? How can I make sure she feels at home and does not wander away?
LORNA FROM LIVERPOOL

- **Write another letter asking questions about a pet.**
- **With a partner, research the answers and write the reply.**

Teachers' note This activity links with writing letters for real purposes, on page 62. You could discuss how the style and tone of these letters is different from a more personal letter. Link this with the purpose of the letter and produce some hints to display in the classroom, on writing letters for a variety of audiences. The children's letters could be made into a non-fiction book.

Fact and opinion

Pilar found these facts about Camelot Castle on a CD-ROM.

When Pilar visited Camelot, she read this in a tourist leaflet.

Camelot Castle
Explore England's finest and most beautiful castle ruin. Discover its historic past, rich with famous names and blood-curdling events. Wander amazed through the vast rooms once used to lavishly entertain Queen Elizabeth's court. Experience a fascinating and educational journey through a romantic age of glory.

- **Underline five adjectives which show the point of view of the writer of the tourist leaflet.**
- **On another piece of paper, copy and complete the chart. Choose words or phrases which show the writer's point of view. Separate the writer's opinion from the facts.**

Word or phrase	The impression it gives	The facts
finest	It is the best in the country	It is one of many castles in the country

- **Write a list of facts about your school.**
- **Write a description of your school as a leaflet to attract tourists.**

Teachers' note This is an opportunity to link with the language of persuasion and advertising. Ensure that the children are aware that language can be manipulated in such texts and that everything they read is not 'the truth'. Ask them to write a series of facts about a place or building. Then they could take a turn at selling it, manipulating language to become persuasive in tone.

Persuasive language

- **Use this sheet to help you plan your persuasive writing.**

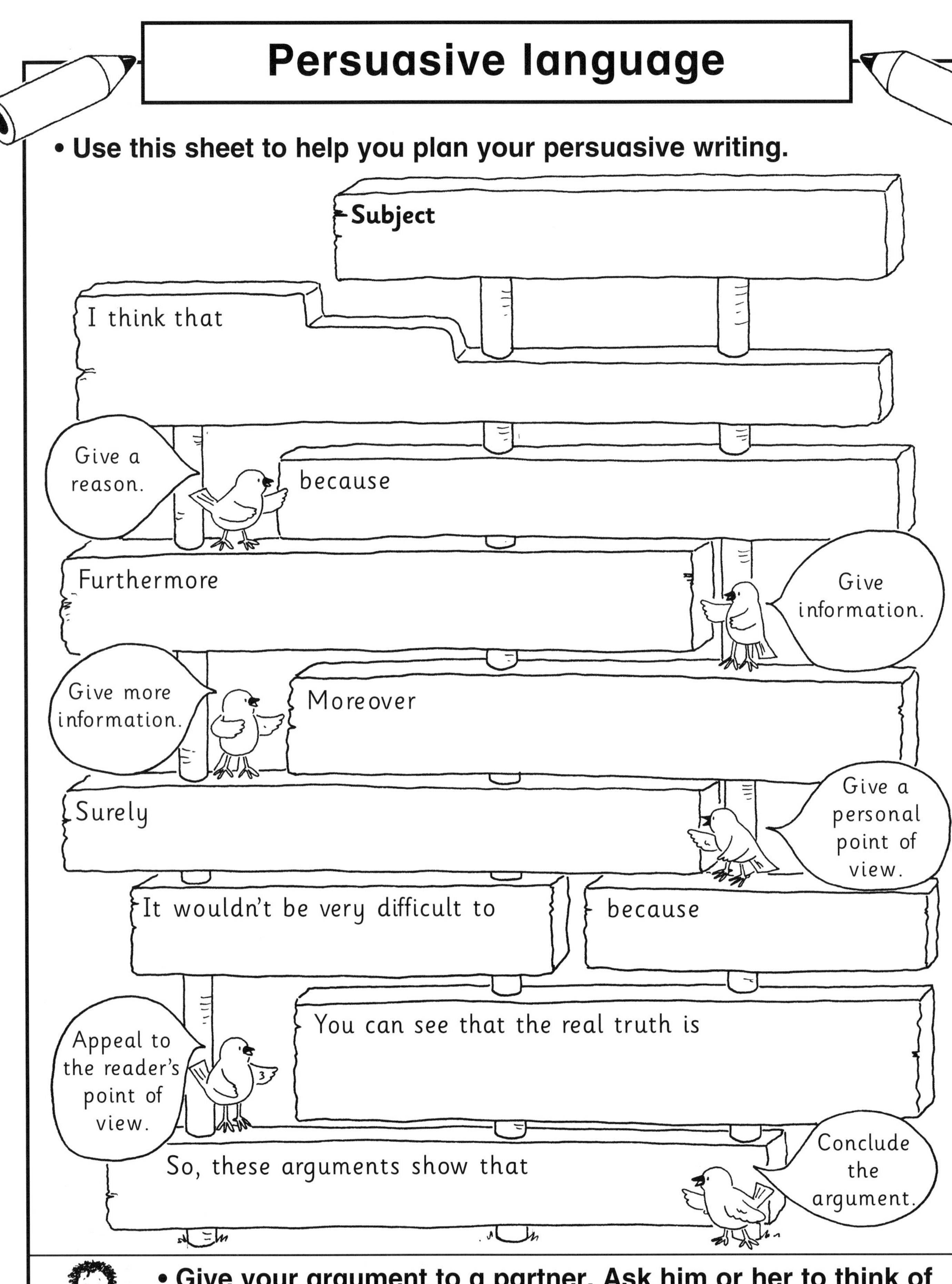

- **Give your argument to a partner. Ask him or her to think of arguments against your point of view.**
- **Make a list of the words which are the most 'persuasive'.**

Teachers' note You could ask the children to collect and investigate words from shared reading which are used as persuasive devices, such as rhetorical questions, key words and phrases which encourage the reader to accept the point of view, for example, 'surely'. The children could collect a range of texts and evaluate those which aim to persuade.

Writing a recount

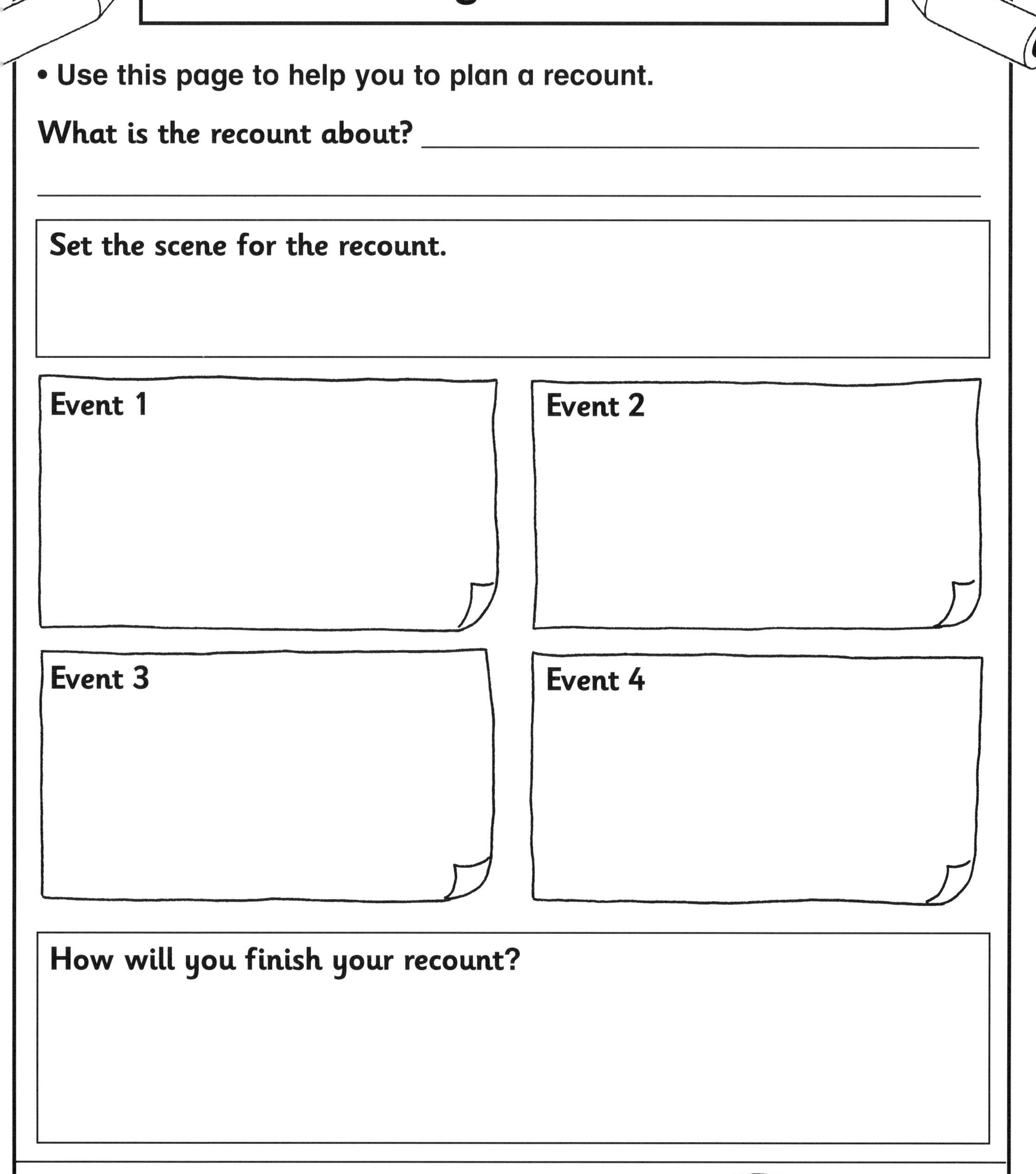

• Use this page to help you to plan a recount.

What is the recount about? ______________________

____

Set the scene for the recount.

Event 1

Event 2

Event 3

Event 4

How will you finish your recount?

• **Write your recount in full.**

Which connectives will you use?

Which tense will you use?

• **Add diagrams and pictures to make your recount clearer.**

You could use a word-processor to make a final copy.

Teachers' note Discuss with the children the purpose of a recount text: to re-tell for information or entertainment. You could model the structure and characteristics in a shared text: scene-setting, events in chronological order, use of the past tense. It might be useful to compare the features with those of a fictional narrative recount.

A personal experience

- **Read Junior's notes about his trip to the Egypt department at the British Museum.**

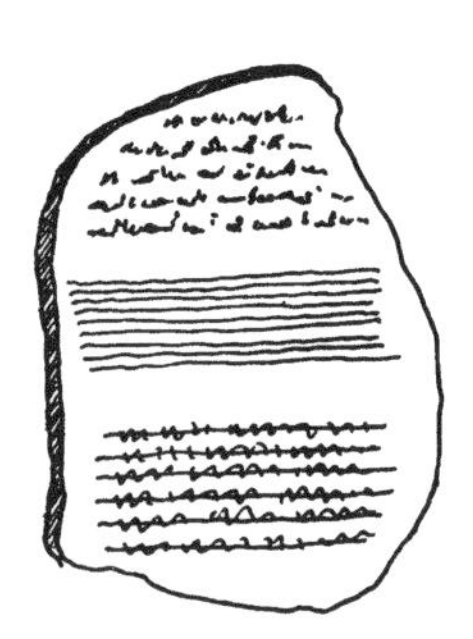

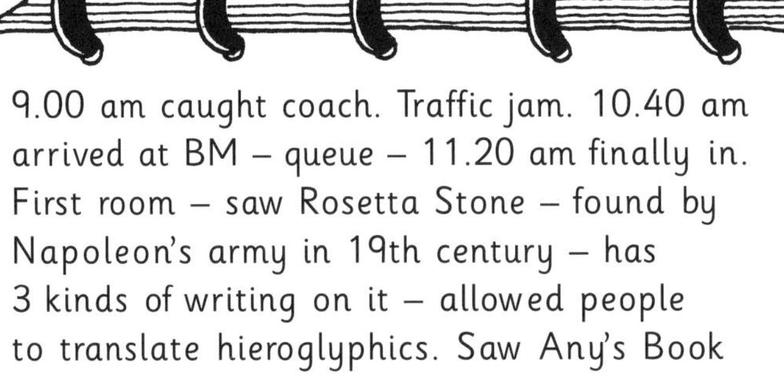

9.00 am caught coach. Traffic jam. 10.40 am arrived at BM – queue – 11.20 am finally in. First room – saw Rosetta Stone – found by Napoleon's army in 19th century – has 3 kinds of writing on it – allowed people to translate hieroglyphics. Saw Any's Book of the Dead – papyrus scrolls – shows working in the fields – tools they used, etc. Lunch – sandwiches – Tracy got lost. 2.00 pm – mummy cases – thousands of years old – spells written on outside. Saw toys – tops, wooden toys – not just about mummies! Back on coach 3.00 pm. Tired – too much to see – must go back. Back home 4.00 pm.
Great day!

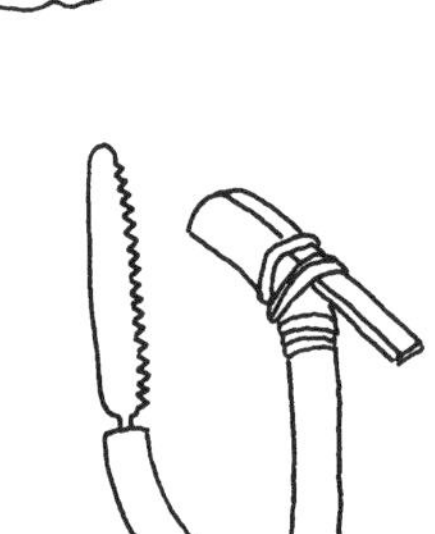

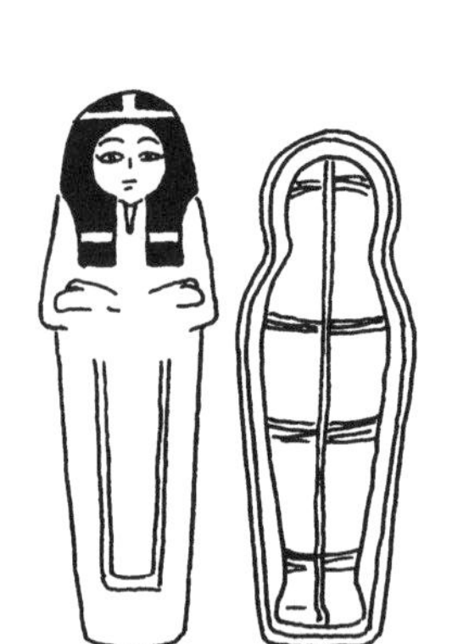

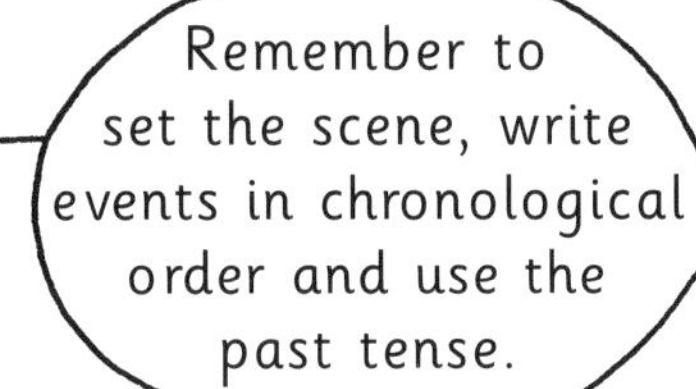

- **Using Junior's notes, write his account of the trip in sentences.**

My trip to discover Ancient Egypt at the British Museum

Continue on another piece of paper if necessary.

- **Write a recount giving information about a visit you have made.**

Teachers' note To extend the activity you could ask the children to re-write parts of their recounts in a different tense or to re-tell parts of their account in a different order. Discuss what happens and whether they are still communicating their meaning to their reader.

Different audiences and purposes

- Choose an entry from each column of the chart. The entries you choose should make sense together.
- Talk to a partner about the style of writing which would suit your text-type, audience, purpose and subject.
- Write the text.

Text-type	Audience	Purpose	Subject
A letter	your teacher	to entertain	about the environment
A report	a six-year-old	to explain	about playing a sport
A story	a newspaper editor	to show your feelings	about your school
A newspaper article	your best friend	to complain	about a place you went on holiday
A leaflet	an 80-year-old	to instruct	about the curse of Tutankhamun's tomb

Teachers' note Select one entry from each section of the chart to model the activity. What would be the language and stylistic demands of the audience and purpose of the piece of writing? The children could discuss how a change of audience impacts upon the way in which the subject matter is treated.

Writing and testing instructions

- **Read the instructions for making a paper plane.**

- **Put them in the correct order.**

Fold down the paper on each side and crease it carefully to form the wings.

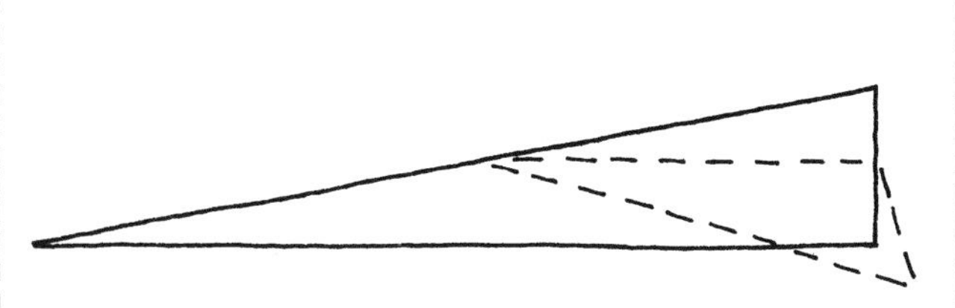

Fold the corners C and D into the centre fold.

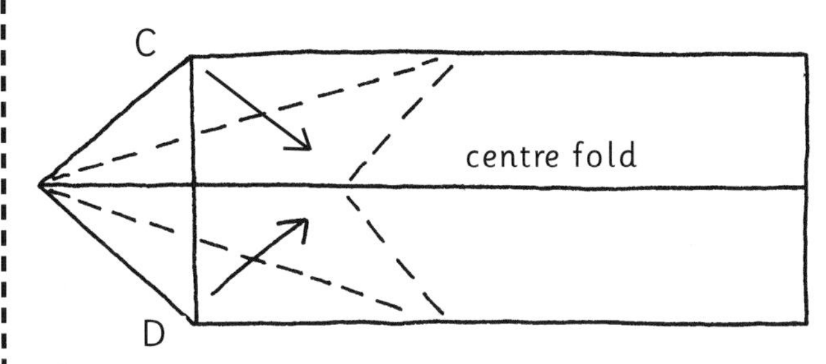

Fold the corners A and B into the centre fold.

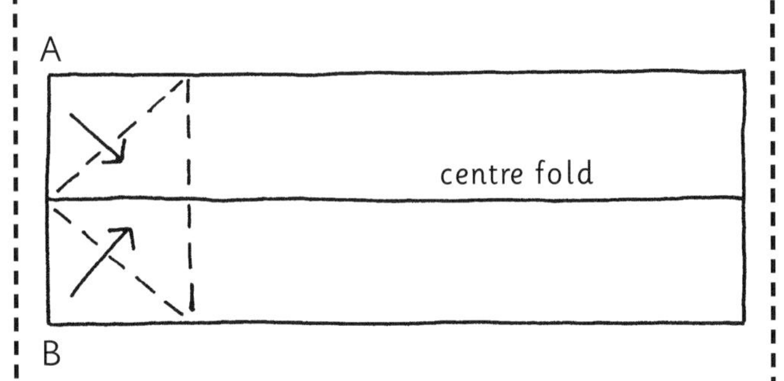

Fold E and F into the middle, lift the wings to the horizontal position and launch!

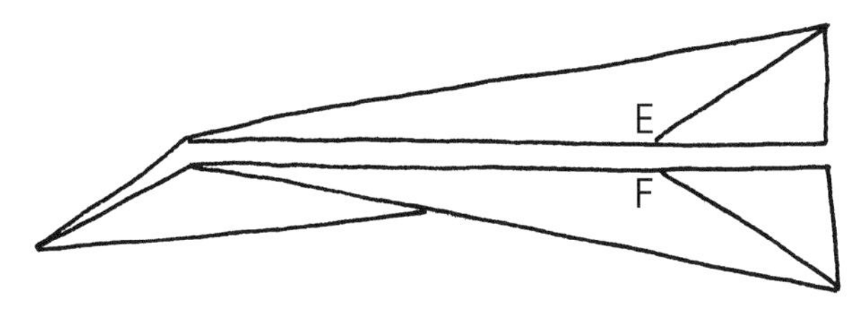

Fold a rectangle of paper in half and open it out again.

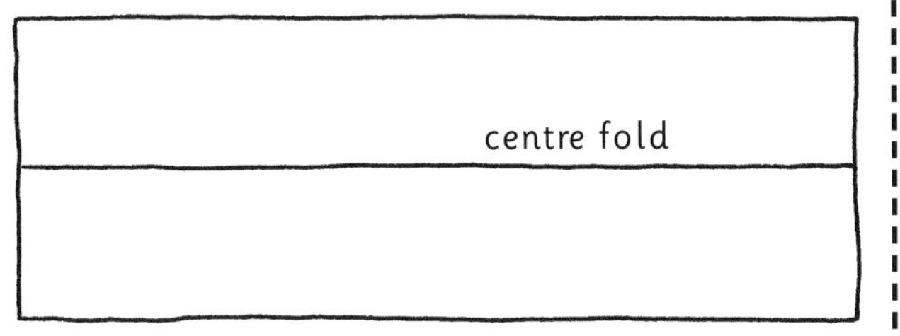

Fold along the centre fold and press the corners E and F together.

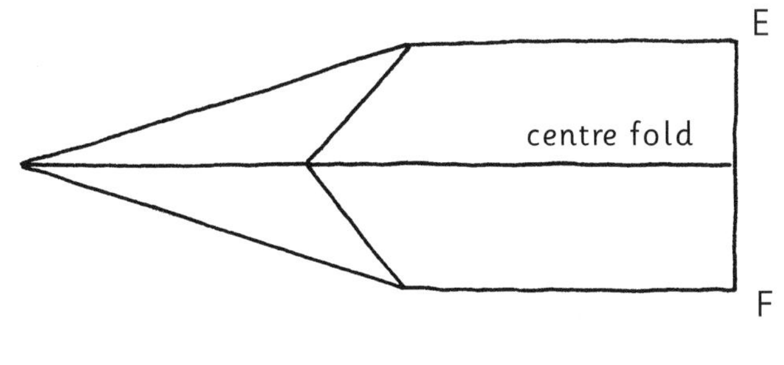

- **Now make the plane. Did you put the instructions in the correct order? Were the instructions accurate? What problems did you face?**

Teachers' note As an introduction to the activity you could discuss the features of instructions, such as sequential order and use of the imperative. Ask the children what might happen if any of these features were missing. As an additional extension activity the children could write a set of simple instructions for making something else and test them out.

Giving instructions

- **Look at the map.**
- **Give the people instructions to reach where they have to go.**

M25
Junction 20
Sports Centre
Honey Street
A1 Main Street
Bishopsgate Station
North Street
Business Centre
Eden Road
A3 South Street
Reservoir
Fast food Restaurant
French Street
A2 West Street
March Avenue
Epping Road
N

I want to get to the Business Centre by car from the M25 motorway.

Leave the M25 at Junction 20.
Drive south along Main Street.
Turn left into Honey Street.

- **Find two more places on the map which the people might want to go to. Write instructions for them.**

Teachers' note You could ask the children to instruct one another in very simple routes – even around the classroom – and for others to follow their instructions exactly. In this way they will discover the importance of proceeding step by step and not missing out any stages. The children could list the features of a variety of instructional texts – from recipes to giving directions.

Making notes

- **Read the passage and the questions in the boxes.**
- **Underline the answers in the text.**
- **Write the information in the boxes.**

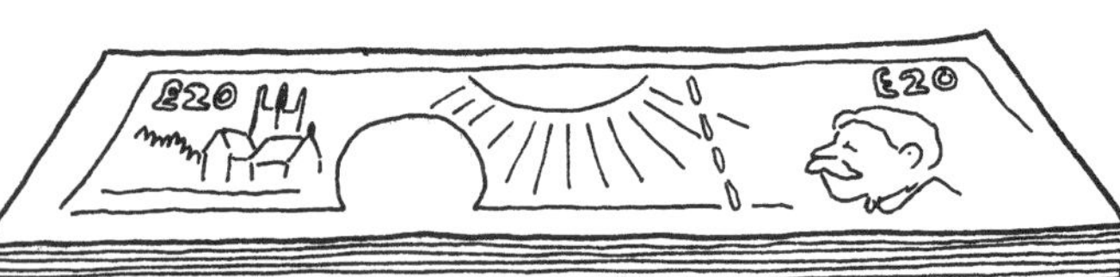

In 1999, the Bank of England produced a new £20 note. They did this to stop criminals copying £20 notes. The new design is virtually impossible to forge. Experts at the Royal Mint have included tiny details on the drawing of composer Edward Elgar which is found on the new note. This has replaced the portrait of scientist Michael Faraday. The Bank has also added a hologram and a red and green fluorescent number 20, which you can only see under the ultraviolet light of special security machines.

Who?
The Bank of England

What?
New £20 note

When?

Why?

Which main design feature?

Which extra features?

- **Write out your notes in sentences. Use your own words.**

Use a dictionary. Find the meanings of hologram; fluorescent; ultraviolet.

Teachers' note Encourage the children to ask themselves basic questions about a non-fiction text and to underline key facts. Writing the information in another form also gives more of an opportunity for the children to write in their own words rather than copy out the original text.

Abbreviations track

Abbreviations are very useful for note-taking.

- **Write on the track the correct versions of the abbreviations.**

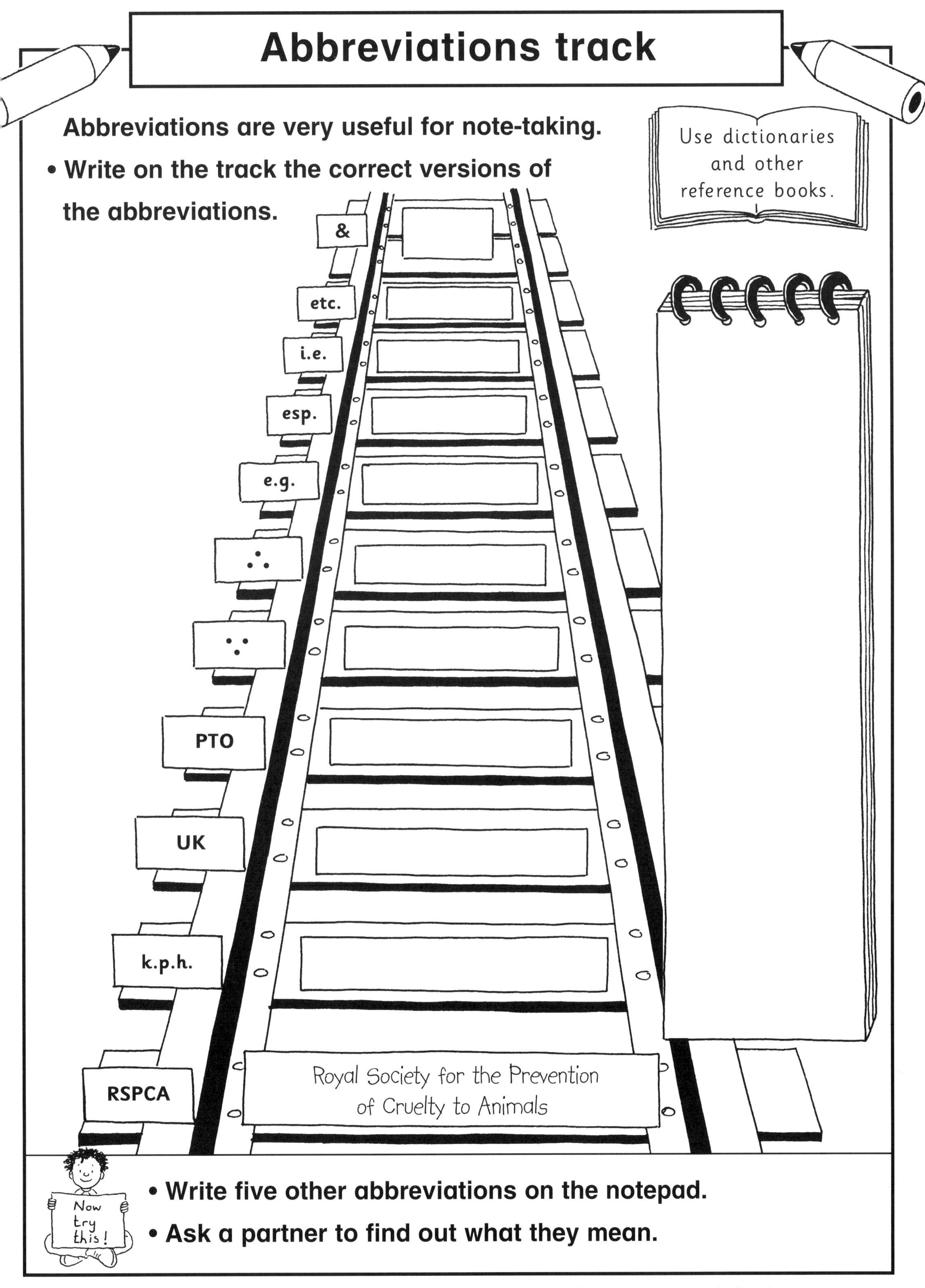

- **Write five other abbreviations on the notepad.**
- **Ask a partner to find out what they mean.**

Teachers' note To introduce the activity discuss abbreviations used in note-taking and what these mean. This can link with word derivation at word level. You could make a list of these abbreviations and display them in the class for constant use. Children could collect their words and make a class 'Abbreviations Dictionary' for reference use.

Writing up your notes

Mr Jackson is planning a sponsored walk to raise money for a minibus. He wants to persuade other people that this is a good idea.

- **Read his notes. Use them to write a speech to persuade others.**

Aim – raise as much £ as poss. for minibus (suitable for wheelchairs) – good cause – needed for children's sports teams – walk = quick way to make £ – one person in charge of publicity – pupils to make posters – pupils to walk – 50p a km

first aid posts needed on walk – drinks needed at various stages – volunteers needed – cars needed to help those who drop out – everyone gets a cert. – around local park – start and finish at school

date 17 June – 9 sharp start – police need to give permission – collect money from forms (need to print forms) – needs to be done quickly

Ladies and Gentlemen...

Continue on another sheet of paper if necessary.

- **Write a letter to the local newspaper, asking for volunteers for the sponsored walk. Use the same notes.**

Teachers' note This activity focuses on the need to make clear notes but also on the fact that all notes will be written up for a specific purpose. The style of the writing will reflect that purpose. In the plenary session you could ask the children to reflect on the different stylistic features needed for different purposes.

An explanation

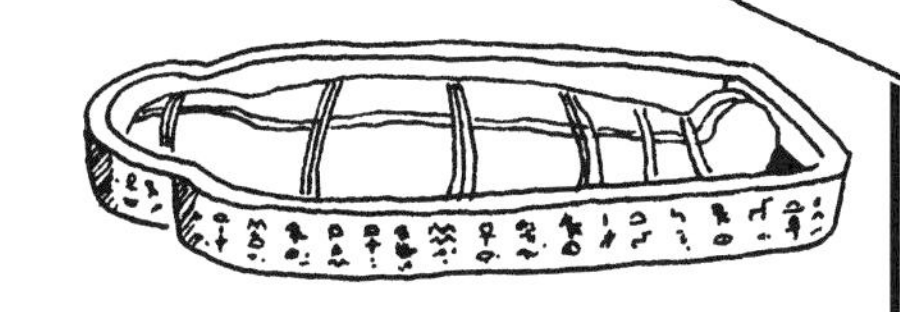

- **Cut out the strips. Put them in the correct order, using the questions to help you.**

For Ancient Egyptians, the body of a dead person had to be preserved so that it could be recognised in the afterlife. The word 'mummy' comes from an Arabic word which means 'bitumen', a kind of black tar. Mummies often looked so black that the Arabs thought they were made of tar.

Next, the body had to be slowly dried out so it would not rot. Remember the human body is 75% water. To do this, the body was packed in natron crystals – a kind of salt. This slowly removed water from the body, dissolved fats and kept the skin supple.

The mummy was then placed in its final coffin. This was not just a container. It was covered in magical texts to protect the body in the afterlife.

Firstly, after death, the body was not buried for 70 days. It was given to embalmers, who removed the brain and other internal organs – the parts which would rot more easily. The brain was removed through the nostrils, so that the skull did not have to be cracked. The internal organs came out through a small cut in the left side. The idea was to keep the body as whole as possible. All these body parts were also preserved and kept in jars for placing in the tomb.

Then, before the body was bandaged, it was massaged with lotions and expensive perfumes and coated with resin.

When this drying process was complete – usually in about 15 days – the body cavity was filled with sweet-smelling spices, sawdust and linen. The cut in the side was sewn up.

Then a mask was placed over the face. This was so that the body could be identified by the spirits who would return to the tomb. The final layer on top of this was usually a mixture of linen and plaster which would set hard. Sometimes this was covered in gold.

Another 15 of the 70 days were given over for the bandaging of the body. More than 324 square metres of linen might be used. Charms and prayers were often wrapped in with the bandages. Head, fingers, toes and the rest of the body were all wrapped with care.

What comes first in an explanation?

In what sort of order should an explanation be written?

Which words at the beginning of each paragraph tell you what should come next?

- **Write an explanation of a process or sequence of events. Use the features you have learned about on this page. Which verb tense will you use?**

Teachers' note You could use an explanation as a shared text and discuss its features – chronological order, using connectives which logically lead you on to the next stage, often written in the present or the passive tenses. Play games in which children follow a written explanation absolutely; what stops them understanding how to carry out the process?

A letter with a purpose

- **Read these two extracts. They show what life was like for poor children in nineteenth-century England.**

Workhouse menu			
	Breakfast	**Dinner**	**Supper**
Sunday	1 pint of gruel (porridge) daily, thickened with flour; 3–5oz bread daily	4–6oz beef, 3oz bread, veg.	3–5oz bread daily; butter, milk and water daily
Monday		10–14oz boiled suet pudding	
Tuesday		4–5oz boiled mutton, veg.	
Wednesday		4–6oz beef, veg.	
Thursday		12–14oz rice pudding	
Friday		4–6oz boiled mutton, veg.	
Saturday		1 pint soup, 3oz bread	

ENFIELD PARISH WORKHOUSE, 1827

Punishment in school
It is common to fasten the legs of offenders together with wooden shackles. The shackle is a piece of wood about a foot long and tied to each leg. Pupils are ordered to walk around the schoolroom until tired out.

JOSEPH LANCASTER: IMPROVEMENTS IN EDUCATION, 1803

- **Imagine you are a Member of Parliament in the nineteenth century.**
- **Underline the things you think need bringing to people's attention.**
- **Write a letter to complain about the way children are treated.**

Sir,
I must write to you about the appalling conditions which exist today in...

Think about the features of letter style you will use:
– give two or three reasons to back your argument;
– include evidence to support your views;
– end your letter by stating your point of view again.

- **Think of a modern-day issue to do with the treatment of children.**
- **Write a letter to the Editor of a local newspaper about it.**

Teachers' note To introduce the activity you could model the various stages in letter-writing, paying special attention to the intended audience, as the style of letters will change according to recipient. The children could role-play characters in the example – what would the workhouse beadle say? How would the nineteenth-century teachers respond?

A leaflet

- **Leaflets tell us important things in a simple and attractive way. They usually try to persuade us.**
- **Write the correct labels from the checklist in the boxes.**

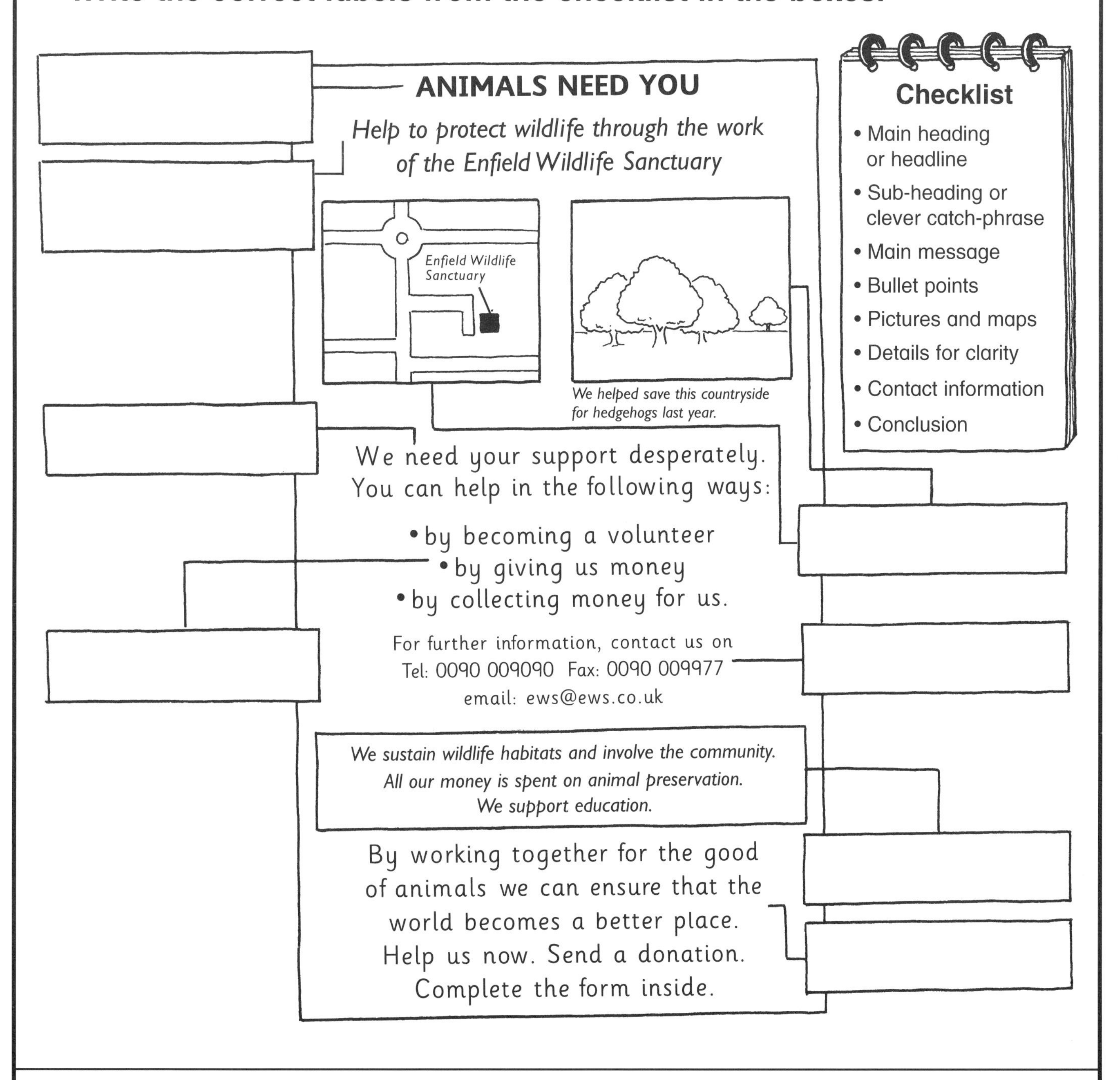

- **Design and write a leaflet for a charity, using the same features. Try to persuade people to give money to the charity.**

Teachers' note You could discuss with the children the features of a variety of leaflets and their purposes. Select examples of the kind of language used for various purposes, for example, persuasive for leaflets which are trying to extract money; instructive for those which are telling the public something. Discuss how design features, such as bullet points, affect a text.

Preparing a talk

- Use this sheet to prepare a talk for your class.

Subject

- Make notes in the boxes. Use abbreviations.

Abbreviations word-bank

e.g.	for example
i.e.	that is
∴	therefore
∵	because
+	plus
&	and
etc.	and so on
esp.	especially

Introducing the topic

First main point

Second main point

Third main point

Conclusion

- Practise your talk with a partner.
- Think of ways to make your talk clearer and more interesting.

Teachers' note The focus here is to enable the children to gather information to give a talk but not be overloaded with detail. This sheet structures their work and also acts as an aide-memoire for useful abbreviations. When the children give their talks, you could allow others to comment constructively on how the presentation and content could be improved.